C000099197

22
FLOORS

22
FLOORS

DAVID WATSON

Riverside Publishing Solutions

David Watson asserts his moral right to be
identified as the author of this book.

Published by Riverside Publishing Solutions, Salisbury, UK
Copyright © 2019 David Watson

Printed and bound in the UK

22 Floors paperback edition
ISBN: 978-1-9995853-9-6

Also available as Kindle edition
ISBN: 978-1-913012-00-7

This is a work of fiction. Names, characters, businesses, places,
events and incidents are either the products of the author's
imagination or used in a fictitious manner. Any resemblance to actual
persons, living or dead, or actual events is purely coincidental.

All rights reserved. No part of this publication may be reproduced,
distributed, or transmitted in any form or by any means, including
photocopying, recording, or other electronic or mechanical methods,
without the prior written permission of the publisher, except
in the case of brief quotations embodied in critical reviews and
certain other non commercial uses permitted by copyright law.

CONTENTS

ABOUT THE AUTHOR

For 20 years, David Watson has solved problems for companies and individual clients. He has a unique way of helping people look at their problems and, after time, his way of helping becomes the solution. Every problem is unique and so is the solution. Through his long career in customer services and care work, David has always focused on the individual person, bringing understanding to their issues and tailoring his approach. He believes everything in life is a form of customer service and is passionate about simple steps to help people and companies understand they are the key to the difference they wish to make.

David helps his clients to identify their integrity and the things that matter to them. And because he continually explores his curiosity for the world, he doesn't shy away from writing books to make sense of the world and parts of life he doesn't understand. Instead he explores the endless unknown, as that is where the questions are and the answers lie. David acknowledges his thought processes, accepts his spiritual view of life and realises sometimes there is a conflict and a bridge that needs to be built to move forward. Spiritualism, life and companies have to grow. We cannot stagnate and expect balance. If you have an itch to be doing something different, go and scratch it!

Word-of-mouth is crucial for any author to succeed. If you enjoyed the book, please leave a review on Amazon. Even if it's just a sentence or two. It would make all the difference and would be very much appreciated. For further information and regular blog updates, go to www.davidwatsonauthor.com

David can be found on Facebook by searching for @OfficialDavidWatson

PREFACE

This is my third attempt at trying to tell the story. All three versions, different in their characters and content, but with the same theme, the afterlife. I wanted to write about something else, what that was, I'm not sure. I was hoping for something quick-witted which would be reviewed as smart and a must-read for city hipsters. I so wanted to see a review which described me as capturing the thoughts of society and regurgitating the moment as only the most Bohemian artists can. As is often the case, the heart and soul win through and the ego is silenced. When I write like this, it is very visual, and I would describe it as reciting, more than my own words. It is, as if I am accessing a portal and I can see six souls standing around a well. They talk into this well, and it is connected by a gold line, to the top of my head. I don't mean this to sound bizarre and I don't ask people to believe me; I am, for my own benefit acknowledging the process.

INTRODUCTION

Losing someone can be the most painful experience. This can be made worse by how we lost them. I have spent my life perplexed by the idea of the afterlife, and the older I have become, the more I believe there to be something else after this existence. I strongly believe as humans we are incapable of understanding how this works at this time in our evolution, but only because this form is limited and as such, any explanation must be relevant and a reflection of the world around us. When writing this story, I wanted to explore the dynamics of human life, from the perspective of the soul. It is often quoted, "You do not have a soul, you are a soul, you have a body" and with this in mind, I explored what happens to the soul when the ego sabotages the body (suicide). When a person commits suicide, and if there is some form of afterlife, it would suggest that living in a human body serves a purpose. If this is so, then it makes sense that the process must be completed, to enable the soul to serve out that purpose. So how does this happen? And what might be waiting for the soul?

INTRODUCTION

22ND FLOOR

As I get off the bus, Angie pushes past me.
"Don't mind me," I say.

Angie ignores me. I walk across the road. "It's my baby!" a man shouts. I turn round and the man has grabbed Angie. I ignore them – it's not my concern – and head up the steps into Victoria office block.

"Yes, sir?" the security guard asks.

"Michael Eastman. I have an appointment."

"With whom?" the security guard asks.

"Angel Lighting. Umm, could I ask you to help a young lady outside – just keep a watch over her? Some guy, he seems the physical type... I would watch myself, but I am cutting it fine for my appointment. I need this job."

The security guard looks over his desk and sees Angie standing in the middle of the road, held back by the man.

"Don't worry, sir." The security guard gets up from his desk and heads across the foyer onto the street. As the security guard walks towards the doors, I walk over to the elevator. The doors open and I press button 22.

The elevator stops, the doors open and I take the stairs to the top. As I walk up the last few steps, I am a little nervous. I wasn't expecting this. I hold onto the handrail. There's an old metal-plated door with peeling paint that once kept people in and used to be locked; it is now slightly ajar and doesn't close properly. I open the door and stand on the top of the building. A beautiful blue sky, a few white clouds and a slight breeze greet me up on the roof. In the distance I can hear a container ship sounding its horn. I am standing on top of the building, 22 floors high. I walk to the edge of the roof. To the east I can see the container ship I had heard. It's moving down the estuary, the sun glistening on the water. My nerves have lessened; I am feeling relieved. I take a deep breath and watch the people below: I can see the man and Angie arguing, passers-by watching the two of them squabble. Some have stopped. They are glued to their every move. A thought enters my conscious that people do not really know what is going on. They think they do, but no one is really paying attention. The bystanders are watching the couple argue. They don't know what it is about or who started it. They can hear them shouting and can glean little snippets of information, but is this argument new? Old? Has one of them forgotten an anniversary or foolishly made a promise they couldn't keep? We have all done that. The passers-by watch, not because they care, but because they want the five-minute fix of excitement. Angie and the man, their voices raised, are unconcerned by the audience. Everyone is watching now, even the security guard. Crowds love watching people pull each other apart, then we all go home to tell someone what we saw, post it on Facebook, create a hashtag for Twitter. Some members of the crowd have started holding up their mobile phones to film the couple; gorging themselves on the human suffering that has become our favourite entertainment; the humiliation of others, not because we really enjoy it, but because it's not happening to us. And if you're not the one being laughed at then, you have escaped notice like I have.

Only, I have this continuing feeling of being watched. I have had this feeling for a few weeks now. When I first scouted this building, I felt someone staring at me. It has become more intense recently, but I always look around and see no one. Two nights ago I woke in the night, expecting to find someone in my room; I even got up and searched the house. It is making me jittery and I say aloud to myself, "Take a deep breath, you can't see anyone and no one is here. You are alone." I repeat this three times taking in a deep breath with each sentence. As I pull myself together I stand up, glance over the ledge and step off the building.

I have decided that my time has been and I no longer want to be part of society. Once upon a time, I could switch off and ignore the outside world. I remember work memos arrived on paper and were sent to you through the post, or handwritten and delivered by the office junior. Better still, the boss would come and see you, have a chat. Then someone invented computers, emails, and the days of holding a pencil in my hand have been replaced with plastic keys and a tapping sound. My view is a computer screen and communicates with a *bing* noise to let me know I have another email. My 20-something boss needs to know instantly the stats on some project or other, but he can't get up and walk 20 yards across the open plan floor to ask me. I was in an elevator with him last week and he asked me what floor I wanted, when I told him I was in his department he wasn't even embarrassed that he didn't know me. This new age of communication has reduced humans to computer profiles and people becoming nervous when you say good morning at the bus stop. I can't remember the last time someone looked me in the eye to talk.

I have decided my time has been. This is my choice. I have had enough of living and my place in the world. The view of the road beneath me is different now I am falling. The wind was rushing past me but now everything is starting to slow down. I wasn't expecting this. I thought it would be a frenzied panic. My feelings about stepping off the roof are still strong and I haven't thought this was a terrible mistake. I am comfortable with what I have done.

A few years ago I started to feel despondent and this became my way of life. I would wake in the morning, if I managed to sleep at all, and before I opened my eyes I would sigh. Lifting my head off the pillow required a conversation with myself, listing the many reasons it had to be done. It wasn't long before I couldn't find any reasons I cared about. After a while, you notice weeks, and then months, have passed since you last smiled. The last time I remember having a good old belly laugh I think I was a child. Imagine the feeling you have on a bleak winter's day, the dreariness you feel inside, a glum weight preventing you from lifting yourself, your chin so heavy it is sitting on your chest and you are permanently slumping forward. Gone are the days of standing up straight and walking with a spring in your step.

When I visualise my mood, I see a rainy day and a park bench. The bench is next to a path. I cannot see what is behind the bench or the view in front of me, and I always view myself from the side as if from a distance. In my mind, I have tried to walk up to the bench and talk to myself, but I am unable to get close. I used to shout out in frustration, trying to catch my own attention. I believed if I could just speak to this side of myself, I could convince him to change our environment, maybe take a walk with me. We would go off in search of some sunshine. We could collaborate together, negotiate a balance. Once, after reading a self-help book, I created a plan. I practised visualised meditation, hoping for some relief. I went to the library and scoured books for images of beautiful places around the world. I wrote down the intricate details of each picture, and at home I started to meditate. I saw myself sitting on a park bench, and the two of us went off on a mountain hike through lush forest. I created flowers which could change colour and shape, nothing was fixed, and there were no rules. I was governed only by my passion and imagination. As we walked up one path, the flowers lifted up as we passed as in a Mexican wave. As we approached a large rock and the path turned, the sun warmed my face. At the bottom of the hill, all the colours of the rainbow glistened in the stream. We continued up the path, the flowers growing tall, then sinking to the ground at the bottom of their stalks, shaking like a cat preparing to pounce. Somehow they propelled themselves off the ground like fireworks and exploded in the air. With every fire-work flower exploding, new ones fell to the ground, an array of different colours tumbling like snowflakes. As they landed, covering the ground, they grew again, and then fired back into the sky. Every colour I have ever imagined was falling from the sky around me, shooting hundreds of feet into the air, looking like dai-sies, roses, carnations, tulips, lilies... It was an endless colour extravaganza. Soon I could hear them whistle as they flew upwards, falling to the ground, giggling as they landed, wiggling their stalks, ready to launch once more into the sky. I looked at my grey friend, unimpressed with all he sees. I grab his hands and shout: "Come on! This is great!"

I dance around Mr Grey, taking him by both hands, twirling him round, trying to muster a smile from his face. Nothing. My grey companion just stands there in his grey trilby and grey overcoat. As the hundreds of different colours land on Mr Grey, they dissolve of their colour and fall from him, like old house dust. I smile, regardless. I have not enjoyed myself so much for ages. My imagination has reached new highs, and I have created excitement, fresh new hope. I am running and leaping like a spring lamb continuing upwards, determined to show Mr Grey this endless joy, the opportunities from within the mind we share to recreate passion and let it flood into our everyday lives. I stand in front of Mr Grey and imagine my joy and try to send it to him. Slowly, a shimmering energy filters from my body and into Mr Grey, and as it does, some of the dust on his cheeks disappears and I can see colour in his face. The colour is very faint, but slowly it starts to show glimpses of the person underneath the grey.

As we reach the summit of the mountain, I make my way through the trees and the ground turns to sand. I find myself on a beach. To my left is a waterfall, falling into the sea. The waves lap gently onto the white sand,

and the sun sets on the horizon, a beautiful golden sky reflecting off the clear ocean water. I didn't know it was possible to create such vivid pictures, experience feelings, and to make it all seem so real. The golden light floats on the surface of the water and I sit down to absorb this glorious feeling. Mr Grey sits next to me. We are both watching the sunset. A golden light shows the colour in his face and for the first time he looks back at me. I see a tired face, my face. Mr Grey places a hand on my shoulder, raises his eyebrows to heaven, and sighs. As he does so, the grey spreads onto my shoulder, I feel the dust seep into my body, my breathing becomes difficult. The sun disappears from the horizon and I can no longer feel its warmth. My colourful world turns grey, the sands, to dust. I look to Mr Grey and he has gone. I stand up: he is nowhere to be seen. I feel weighed down, I have a trilby on, I am wearing an old overcoat, and my hands look familiar. I realise I am Mr Grey, we are one, he is not my friend or my companion, he is my passion drained, he is my love that has gone, my kaleidoscope of colours expressed as emotions slipped away. My soul is a tired old man, no longer able to enjoy life.

I am sitting on the bench again. The rain is coming down hard now. I see a reflection of myself in a raindrop that has formed on the peak of my hat. As it drops towards the ground, I see the colourful me trapped inside. As I watch the raindrop fall, I see myself panicking scratching at the walls so hard my fingers bleed scarlet red. For a moment, I see the beauty of this red, so deep in colour, my life bleeding away through my fingertips. The raindrop hits the floor. In an instant it is gone, and just like that, so am I. This is the moment Mr Grey takes control. I cannot escape and he will not be turned. I will sit on the bench and let the rain pour down onto me.

This is when it happened. The day I decided I had had enough. I took the challenge to Mr Grey, I showed him the power of our imagination, the beauty that was available for us to create, and he placed his hand on my shoulder. I looked him in the eye and saw the truth. I had let the colour slip away from me a long time ago, and with it my life.

21ST FLOOR

As I pass the window of the 21st floor, I again get a feeling of being watched. This time though, I see the reflection of my father in the glass. I turn round to see him, but he is not there. My father died many years ago, and probably died quite lonely, although I am not sure. There were people at his funeral but none seemed that upset; most appeared to be there out of duty, as was I, really. I had not enjoyed conversations with my father for many years, and when we did talk it was often quite painful. We never argued, we just never had anything in common except that we were related. I didn't hate my father, at least, not anymore. Talking with my father would consist of silences very similar to bumping into an old work colleague or friend; once upon a time you frequently spoke to this person, maybe even every day, especially work colleagues. Forty hours a week sharing an office, and then one of you leaves, and several years later, a random event like shopping in the supermarket brings you together. The meeting starts well: "How are you? What are you doing now? Have you seen what's-his-name lately?" But you run out of things to say after five minutes. You stand there awkwardly for five minutes more, before you decide enough is enough, tell them it was nice to see them, and the two of you should try to catch up some time. Really, when it comes down to it, you were never actually friends, you were two people thrown together by circumstance. My father and I are two such people; we have never been friends, we were tied together because he is my father. As a child, we had daily inter-action, though I am not sure we ever spoke past the events of the day. Once I became an adult I left home, and we quickly stopped bothering with each other. There were family days like Christmas, and I would arrive at home, shake hands with my father, exchange pleasantries. These occasions were really just a result of our national obsession with families being together for the festive season. I am sure many of us would rather ignore the festive season, and just spend time on our own. Of course, to do this would take a massive overhaul of our social conditioning, beginning with childhood. Constantly bombarded with Christmas songs, wishing everyone a merry Christmas, and films telling the story of families being reunited, the loving bond "normal" families have... What I remember about Christmas when I was a child is dinner, small talk and watching TV. As I grew up, and before I married, I stopped doing any of this, and quickly learnt not to mention to my friends that I would be spending Christmas alone. Initially this would bring about sympathy, until they discovered it was my own idea. Then they would turn, and I would be chastised for being miserable and not getting into the Christmas spirit. I'm not sure if I felt this was my father's fault for never seeming interested in what I was doing. I think some men simply shouldn't have children: my father was never a child-beater or a heavy drinker, and to my knowledge he never abused my mother. He was just never interested. He would come home from work, pick up whatever book he was reading, sit in his chair and read, rarely ever lifting his head over it to see his son growing up. I think my father would have been a happier man if he had never had children, and maybe actually did some of the things he loved to read about. This was probably the story for many of his generation; they met, fell in love, got married had a kid, and that's your lot. For some, this was all they needed in life, a sort of natural order, a result of social expectation of the times. Social expectations haven't changed all that much, we have just become more lenient with the rules. When discussing someone else's business in the local shop, the neighbours no longer gasp or ignore you as you walk past them going about your business looking for baked beans. No one cares if you divorce, no one gets ostracised from society because the father has left the mother. It has become commonplace across the playgrounds for fathers to turn up on a Friday and collect the different kids from different mothers, or at least those who can be bothered. Who would have thought my brother from another mother would have become commonplace statement of fact. Has it ever occurred to these people to not have kids? Maybe if my father had been around in these more lenient times he could have just paid maintenance and become whoever he wanted to be.

So there I am one day, stood by the side of a hole, watching the coffin of my father going into the ground, trying my best to seem respectful when actually I am bored and putting the world to rights in my own judgemental way, an observation with little knowledge or understanding of the facts. I always felt sad that I wasn't closer to my father; surely it is natural to grow up expecting to be friends with your dad? I remember exactly when I realised I was turning into my father. I had been working long hours for many months; this was starting to take its toll on me. I hadn't noticed the long days – seven a week had become my routine. I woke in the morning, went to work, came home, trudged upstairs, poked my head through the bedroom door to look at the kids – a gesture to myself and my wife; it helped me sleep easier at night. James, my son, was about four, and excited as four-year-olds are at Christmas. This particular Christmas morning, I was woken by the screams and laughs of the kids downstairs. I rolled over and pulled the duvet over my head to try and sleep. I could hear James playing with his new toy. It made a loud whistling noise followed by a bell ringing and I knew I wouldn't be getting a lie-in today. I got up and headed downstairs. "Daddy, Daddy!", James shouted as he ran towards me. "Daddy, help me!", James said holding out a half-open present.

"In a minute," I replied as I stepped around the inconvenience in my way.

James ran off, picked up his fire engine, a gift from Aunt Mabel, and came running over to me, pressing the siren, proudly lifting up his new fire engine. "Daddy!"

"James! Go away!", I shouted.

Stunned, James lowered the fire engine. "Sorry Daddy," he murmured through his quivering lip.

I walked into the kitchen and put the kettle on. I didn't know what we had given the kids for Christmas. I hadn't been involved in any of the Christmas planning, hadn't been involved in anything for a long time. The kettle clicked and I started to pour the water into my mug. I caught my reflection in the kettle. I was unshaven, blood-shot eyes, pasty skin. This isn't James's fault; I am exhausted I thought to myself. I made my cup of tea, walked into the sitting room, picked up James, gave him a big hug and sat him down next to me.

"Show me what Santa brought you, son," I told him.

I looked over to my wife and mouthed, "I'm sorry".

The rest of the day was spent playing with the kids, the following day I phoned in sick and didn't return to work until after New Year. That was my moment.

As I wonder if my father ever had a moment, my attention snaps back to the now, falling to the ground. I see my mum and dad in the window I am passing. They are much younger sitting on a picnic blanket; my dad is smiling and my mum is gazing at him. I never saw my mum and dad like this, looking at each other in love.

"Mary, I have been to the bank. We've done it. Finally, every penny we need", my dad says.

"All of it? £1500?", my mum asks.

My dad nods with a huge smile on his face. "I've looked at maps; done the sums, we could travel for a couple of years!" my dad tells her.

"I have spoken to Dad and he thinks we're crazy..."

"He would," my dad says, interrupting. "Mary, we have saved for this, worked hard... This is everything we talked about. We planned this trip for us, not so your dad could fill your head with his ideas," my dad says.

"He was only saying it's a lot of money and afterwards we would have nothing," my mum replies.

"Nothing, Mary? We would have experience, memories people look at pictures in books and can only wonder what it could be like. We will be able to say we were there, we saw it with our own eyes, touched the soil, and breathed the air. We would be able to say, 'and just over there out of the picture is the place we stayed!'" my dad says pleadingly.

The reflection fades. I can only guess that my dad failed to convince my mum, I know they never travelled anywhere. Now I think about it that must be how they bought the house all those years ago, with my dad's dreams. Maybe he had his moment after all.

20TH FLOOR

I am 47 years old, I have a daughter and a son, both of whom I am very proud of, and I hope when they discover what I have done they will remember me as someone who was more interested in them than my father was in me. If not, it is too late now!

I am still confused by how slowly everything is moving. I worked out it would be over in seconds, and yet here I am still thinking, reminiscing!

I hear the sound of dogs barking, the wind carrying the sound from somewhere far away. I remember my old dog, Paddy. There was a time when I enjoyed many miles walking through the woods with Paddy as my companion. Nearby my house, the woods were a mix of beeches, oaks, chestnuts, hazels and birch. There was a little of everything, and anytime of the year the woods provided great landscapes for me to admire. The scenery nature had provided as the seasons changed, a rich pallet of tastes, available to anyone who took the trouble to look. From sunsets to sunrises, spring buds and blossoms, green summer leaves turning brown and gold as autumn takes its turn. Finally, winter sets in and reveals the skeleton of the trees, a marvel of different structures, yet all the trees still identifiable from their distinct shape. I first discovered this love for the woodland landscapes with my first dog, a bitch called Molly. She was a mongrel who belonged to an elderly neighbour, Daisy. She kept Molly for company really, and when, sadly, Daisy died, she left a four-year-old Molly with no home. Daisy had children, and when they came to clear out the house we asked what was going to happen to Molly. The daughter said they hadn't really thought about her, and most likely she would be taken to a dog's home. My wife and I suggested, as we had already been looking after her and our children had known her since she was a puppy, we might take her on. Molly was sitting next to me when we had the discussion about keeping her and Daisy's son chipped in, "Well, I don't want her so do what you want."

And with this Molly turned back into the house, wagging her tail and let out a couple of barks. This was the first time I noticed that animals in general know what is happening, and can certainly communicate if you decide to listen. So there it was. We were now the proud owners of a blue, grey, red and white mongrel. Once we had Molly, it was decided responsibility for looking after her should be divided up between the family. Rotas were drawn up. My son would feed her; my daughter would walk her. This lasted about a week, and soon the responsibility became mine, but I didn't mind. I would come in from work, have a quick cup of tea, and take Molly for a walk come rain or shine. If I had had a great day I would tell Molly; if I had had a rough day I told Molly; and this was how it was every day for ten years. For ten years whatever bothered me was left somewhere on those walks. As I look back now there was a pattern: on good days Molly always found a stick for me to throw, and on the bad days she walked by my side. I also believe Molly looked out for me, and when she was thirteen a friend of mine had a bitch that had just given birth to a litter of pups. He came over to my house to persuade me to take one, I was reluctant at first, but Molly came over to me, sat down between my legs, nudged me with her nose, made a low growling whining noise, shifting side-to-side on her front paws, and I was sold. My wife wasn't so excited and the kids weren't bothered. A couple of weeks later I came home with Paddy, a black labrador, and Molly immediately started to mother and train him. All of the things I expected to have to do, Molly seemed to do for me. About a year later, I came downstairs to find that old age had finally caught her up, and Molly had died in her sleep. Because I always believed Molly looked after me, I embraced Paddy in a much different way. I didn't do anything differently with Paddy, I just always felt he was a gift from Molly and appreciated him from the heart. In the early days, I often grieved for Molly, but as the summer came and my walks with Paddy took me through the woods and onto the flower meadows, I found a tree to sit down next to and I would watch Paddy chasing butterflies, leaping though the air. He always kept his mouth closed and would nudge them with his nose, he never seemed to tire and each leap and nudge of a butterfly, fuelled his excitement. As I sat there watching him, listening to the sounds carried by the wind, I would drift away, drift into something which made me feel connected to somewhere else, somewhere different to the environment around me, somewhere much more universal. As time passed and Paddy became older, he no longer leapt in the meadows. The walks through the woods became shorter, and soon he couldn't walk further than the end of the road. Now, when the summer nights set in we would sit in the garden together. I was now more of a companion to my old friend. One day in autumn, I noticed Paddy was not walking very well and was off his food. I took my friend to the vet, a nice chap who was about to deliver the news he delivered on a weekly basis. I imagine it is a well-rehearsed sentence and one the vet never deviates from, "I'm very sorry, you should probably consider what is best for his quality of life..."

It wasn't unexpected. I knew my friend well, and when we pulled up at the vets and I opened the car door for the first time in a few days, Paddy had a spring in his step and pulled on the lead as he headed towards the doors to the vet. They let us straight through into the operating room. Paddy approached the examination table as he had done many times before; his two front paws on top of the table and his back legs bouncing up and down as he tried to jump up. His strength had left him. He looked over to me, and I lifted him onto the table. The vet readied the needle. I held Paddy in my arms, his tail wagged a little and he licked my hand. I told him what a great friend he was and how much I loved him, pulled him tight to my body. He breathed one last time, then his body went limp. If Paddy had a soul, I hoped Molly was waiting for him.

19TH FLOOR

The weeks before I stepped off the roof I hadn't thought about falling. I didn't wonder what would happen, and here I am now, falling past the 19th floor, aware for the first time that I hadn't thought about this part of the process, confused that I even have time to think about this now. If I had asked myself before I stepped off the roof what I imagined would happen, I would not have thought the world would slow down and I would start to see the wind. I would have expected a brief moment of panic then to hit the ground. When I was living, every day I used listen to the wind, and often thought it could tell me stories if I just listened harder. Now I am acutely aware of it, I could tell you the wind has crossed the land, gusted through cities, blowing out the lighter of someone trying to light their cigarette. On a warm day on another continent, in a playful mood it has blown up the skirt of a young lady in a summer dress. It loves to lift sea birds so they can soar high in the sky, before diving down to fill the sails of boats crossing the oceans, or speeding up as it feels land once again. I wonder if this has happened to anyone else when they have decided they no longer want to live. Did they, like me, have a plan? Did they walk a route, decide what train, pick a length of rope because they liked the feel of the fibres? Does the person who pulls the trigger see the puff of smoke before the bullet leaves the barrel? Do they feel the tip of the bullet pressing against them before it pierces the skin, and are they able to track the movement as it moves upwards towards the brain? I never sat around thinking that this was a great idea; it evolved from a feeling. One day, walking past this building, I looked up and saw a place to which I felt drawn. Twice, I made it to the roof and found myself enjoying the view and then looking over the edge. This continued evolving until the day came. I awoke this morning, sat on the edge of my bed, took a deep breath and knew it was today. I then got up, had breakfast and a cup of coffee, put on my suit and caught the bus to this building. It took about fifty minutes, and I enjoyed looking out of the window as I took in the world. I realise now that since having made the decision, I have slept very well. I awoke this morning with a feeling of peace. As I rode along on the bus, I was accompanied by a sense of contentment as if cushioned from harm for the first time. I felt detached from the world but connected to something new. I didn't know what this connection was and I still don't know, although I am feeling closer to something. Maybe just knowing it is finally coming to an end brings me peace.

Still I am left thinking about how I hadn't given any thought to the process, I wasn't even curious. I roll over and look up at the blue sky, wishing I had enjoyed this feeling of elation before I stepped off the roof. A blue sky, a couple of fluffy white clouds. I could be looking up from anywhere in the world – a café in Paris or a little square just off Charles Bridge in Prague, taking in the morning sunshine as I sip my coffee. Should I walk the sights or just sit by the river and watch the tourists go by? I'm not sure, so I will order another coffee while I think about it, staring up at the blue sky and two fluffy white clouds.

"Arrrrgh!" I scream. A jolt goes through my body and I am suddenly aware of what I have done. "Oh hell, Jesus bloody Christ I have jumped off a building!" I say.

My serenity is suddenly gone, and the adrenalin surges through my body. My heart thumps so quickly the beats become a continuous sound, my muscles tense, my arms are flailing and my hands are trying to grip the air to hold onto something, anything, to save myself from falling further.

"We can't stop. We are going to die," a voice says.

"You are going to die," the voice says again.

Everything slows down again, and the serenity returns. I feel happy. I have panicked and it feels like the natural thing to do, to endure a moment of self-preservation. I laugh as I see an image of myself in cartoon form being forced through a doorway, both arms and legs holding onto the doorframe, refusing to budge. Of course this didn't happen to me: I willingly walked through the last door. I had assumed it would be the same as I had seen in films: come to think about it, all of my education of suicide has come from the imagination of Hollywood, and in those films, suicide is always a hanging, a shot to the head or a jumper. Every time I have seen someone falling, panic is guaranteed. But I am not in a film. I am in real life and there is no big airbag at the bottom for the stunt man to fall into. It now seems very clichéd, once someone decided how a falling person should look and it has been copied ever since, yet no one really knows. Is it possible that it's individual for everyone? How can we know?

18ᵀᴴ FLOOR

I see a woman through the window, cleaning the offices, pushing her Hoover in a backwards and forwards motion. The monotony has not yet pierced her well-being and spread like cancer, ripping her apart. She looks at a picture on a desk of two children in fancy dress, big smiles on their faces. She smiles picks the picture up and gives it a wipe with her cloth. She pauses and stares at the photo, and for a brief moment I am sure I see a colour surround her. She puts the photo down and continues with her cleaning, and again I think I can see a colour, not around her, but radiating from her.

I sense she feels no monotony in her life. I wish I could have been the same. I'd wrapped myself up in thoughts of grandeur and never appreciated the quality in my life. I had stopped living with gratitude in my heart. I had always wanted that little bit more and resented others who may have had it. My thoughts of grandeur, the daydreams when I imagined my different life, inspired by a film I had seen or a piece of music

I had heard. The daydreaming turned into wishing my life away as I spent hours and days thinking of endless scenarios. I am always wealthy, loved by everyone, a superhero, a child dragged up by unloving troubled parents but somehow survived, rose above it all and became greater than anyone could have imagined.

Then there's the girl, of course. I got the girl, but not before she jumped through hoops to prove she understood my pain, saw what the rest of the world couldn't. All this effort, wishing these fictional lives were my reality, and I had missed the simple beauty that can be found in a photo. I wonder when I lost this. Was it my wife, Sheila, and the infidelity? I came home to the conversation of how, since the children have grown up and left home, we no longer seem to be a partnership, we no longer seem to have a reason to be together. We were just two people living under the same roof who have long forgotten how they fell in love. At first all was calm: when Sheila told me this, I honestly thought that if she felt this way I should try and be supportive of her. After all, for twenty years she had been a good mother and a good wife. I still saw her as my best friend, hoped that all wasn't lost forever and we would rekindle our relationship. I even thanked her for being honest and asked if she was OK and what did she want to do next. Sheila suggested she went away for a few days to think. I never thought any more about it. Sarah, my daughter, phoned me a couple of days later, distraught and angry.

I tried to reassure her that it would be OK and when her mum returned we would sit down and find a way to start over and make it work. Sarah started sobbing and then shouted down the phone, "Stop, Dad, Mum is with another man."

That was a body blow I hadn't expected. I knew we had both neglected to respect the romance in our marriage, and I'd always assumed we would bumble along. I still tried to reassure Sarah it would all be OK. I must have been shocked and humiliated, but I carried on as if nothing was wrong.

When Sheila returned she was all smiles and said she had had a wonderful time at her friend's. When I told her I had spoken to Sarah, Sheila responded by yelling at me. "I'm single now; Sarah had no right to tell you."

I asked how long it had been going on. I don't remember what she said. She shouted a lot, it was none of my business, it was my fault, and she would take me for everything. I had heard of these scenarios before from divorced colleagues in the office.

A few days later I was brushing my teeth, looking at myself in the bathroom mirror and I started to cry. My legs gave way. I grabbed the basin but I was unable to hold myself up and I fell to my knees. I sobbed, I tried to get up, but sobbed harder, the shock and humiliation were realised. I don't know how long I sobbed for, I'd never sobbed like that before. I felt like a child as I curled up in the foetal position.

Even when I found the strength to stand up, I was unable to maintain any composure. There was about a week of breaking down, always without warning, and a couple of times in public. A couple of months later I came home to find our house missing some belongings. Sheila's new home needed a few things, the savings were cleared out, and a solicitor's letter arrived informing me of our impending divorce. I never spoke to our son James about what happened. I think he saw the difficulties ahead and decided he could do without the pain. For Sarah, it was not so easy. She was really offended by Sheila's actions and it was a few years before they spoke again. Sheila and I have never really spoken since; on the rare occasion our paths have crossed it has been polite, I did try to have a conversation once, but she was still angry about what happened: all those wasted years, and now I had turned the children against her. I wanted to explain that I hadn't spoken to James, and Sarah had her own mind, but she walked away. Now, when I think about it, I understand things just happen, lives change and we cannot always be in love forever, and Sheila wanted to live a full and passionate life. Who doesn't? We all want this, but I still resent being betrayed and being treated as a villain. It's a funny thing, that what bothers me still is not that she left, but how she still resents me and has always blamed me for her unhappiness. I can understand her wanting to be happy; surely that has to be our reason for getting up every day. It is how we sometimes reach this happiness we should question, and then maybe we won't get it wrong.

17TH FLOOR

I smell pipe smoke. My dad used to smoke a pipe. I remember this exotic scent from my childhood. I would watch my dad as he cleaned his pipe, first pulling out his knife and scraping the sides of the bowl, opening up his worn leather pouch, pulling out the tobacco and then teasing it apart and kneading it in his fingers, laying it into the bowl, prodding it down into a nice neat package. Then, finally, his chrome-handled lighter would spark into life, and as he sucked on the pipe, the flame would be drawn into the tobacco. Briefly, the pipe bowl would resemble a small volcano, before he exhaled and released a plume of smoke into the air. It has always seemed strange to me that I loathe the smell of a cigarette, but pipe tobacco smells so nice. An intoxicating scent. I never took up smoking myself. I remember once as a child, stealing some of my father's pipe tobacco and meeting up with my friends, Jimmy and Simon. We had arranged to meet at the cricket pavilion. It was autumn, so we knew no one would be there as everything was locked up until spring. Jimmy and Simon had stolen some cigarettes of their father's and I had an old pipe. Attached to the pavilion was a decrepit shed used for storage and we managed to unhook the latch to break in. Inside we found some thread worn cricket nets and two large grass rollers. We made ourselves comfortable, laid all our goods on the floor and sat staring at our stolen treasure. A couple of times we hastily picked it all up when we heard a noise. It's amazing, as a child, how heightened our hearing becomes when you add in the danger of being caught and the pride of being elected "lookout". There are not many roles of responsibility and authority when you are nine or ten. It took a while for our excitement to simmer down enough that we didn't jump at every noise. As we relaxed, we described in detail and most likely some exaggeration, the risk involved in stealing our treasure. By the time Simon spoke, it had become a James Bond covert operation to foil his evil father. Once we had quietened down we pondered what to do next, each one of us trying to add our expertise without revealing we knew nothing. We all already knew that none of us had ever smoked before. That's how we started on this adventure, out of curiosity!

Jimmy announced he would go first, and Simon and I watched intently as Jimmy placed a cigarette in his mouth. Before it was lit he took a couple of puffs.

"Checking it works," he said confidently. I picked up the box of matches, pulled out a match and struck the side of the box. The igniting sulphur lit the darkened shed, and holding the match to the end of the cigarette, Jimmy nervously inhaled, not gently but a big deep breath filling his lungs. He looked at Simon and me searching for a reaction, all of us wondering what was supposed to happen next.

"My dad never holds his breath." Simon offered as some sort of advice.

Jimmy, unable to hold back the smoke any longer, coughed his guts up and coughed some more. All three of us were rolling around on the floor, Jimmy coughing Simon and I laughing. When Jimmy regained his speech he sat upright looked at the two of us and bold as brass announced, "Go on then, now one of you have a go."

"Not a chance!" we both replied.

Jimmy protested, but Simon and I had seen enough, and we were not about to try and outdo Jimmy today. We left the storage shed, crossed the cricket field and headed towards the woods. There were quicker ways home, but like most young boys our walks home tended to be of a scenic route, more of a wander home. As we walked along the track through the woods, laughing to ourselves as we told Jimmy how his face contorted and went so red he looked like a tomato, we were interrupted.

"Hello girls."

It was Adam Colwaite, our local bully. He had all the normal attributes of a bully: a spoilt boy, bigger than us, older than us and generally nasty to anyone smaller than him, yet butter wouldn't melt in his mouth when his parents were around.

"Do your mummies know their little girls are out playing in the woods?" Adam said, taunting us.

"Does your mum know who your father is?" Simon replied.

Simon wasn't scared of Adam, not like Jimmy and me. Simon was the youngest of six brothers, and he knew how to fight. He would lose, and he knew this, but he also knew his brothers would soon sort out Adam, a fact Adam knew very well too.

"Brave today, aren't we Simon?" he replied.

Simon didn't say anything, he just shrugged his shoulders.

Adam continued, "Well we all know you wouldn't be so brave if you didn't have your brothers around."

"You wouldn't be so brave if my brothers were here," Simon replied.

This time Adam shrugged his shoulders.

"What are you looking at?" Adam said moving his attention to Jimmy and me. I quickly looked down towards my feet. Jimmy just kept staring, too scared to move. Adam often picked on Jimmy, we didn't know why. The last time they met, Adam gave Jimmy a vicious backhand across the face and stood taunting Jimmy as he cried. I was so frightened I would be next, I just stood there and did nothing as the tears rolled down his face, and Adam continued to taunt Jimmy and raise his hand pretending he was going to hit him again.

"Why are you still looking at me? Do you want a kiss? Do you fancy me?" Adam said to Jimmy.

"Just leave us alone," Simon said.

Adam spat at Jimmy and it landed in his eye. Adam laughed and then raised his hand as if to strike. Jimmy cowered down. This was too much for Simon and he leaped forward and punched Adam in the face. Adam was furious and swung a punch at Simon. Simon, well-schooled in the art of fighting bigger boys thanks to his brothers, managed to put his arm up and block the punch. Adam grabbed hold of Simon and they wrestled to the floor. Adam being the bigger and stronger of the two, soon got on top of Simon and started to throw down punches. Simon's arms were covering his face as he tried his best to protect himself.

I looked at Jimmy. The spit on his face had now rolled down to the bottom of his cheek. Jimmy was looking at Adam, raining punches down on his mate. The years of suppressed anger, and possibly the gallant efforts of our mate combined and a surge of bravery roared up through the soles of our feet. We charged. Throwing punches, we ran forwards. One of us connected with Adam and knocked him off Simon. As he fell backwards we continued to throw wild punches. Simon jumped back in, and again showed he was better schooled than us in the art of a good scrap. Adam curled up into the foetal position, but Jimmy and I were not finished yet. We had years of dead legs, dead arms and taunting to repay. Simon had stopped fighting. He stood and watched us, wildly swinging our arms, trying to punch Adam, lucky not to hit each other. Finally, we were exhausted, and as we stood up, Jimmy said, "Oi! Adam," cleared the back of his throat and sinuses and spat the biggest greenie he could muster onto the side of Adam's head. With this last insult repaid, we walked down the track through the woods towards our houses. We didn't really say anything; we looked at each other a lot, I remember big smiles on our faces, and we staggered from side to side as if we were drunk, high on adrenalin, relief and the weight of years of bullying, gone. It was an unbelievable feeling, the exhilaration coursing through our veins, that none of us had ever experienced before, but it is one that bonds you, especially when you're so young.

16TH FLOOR

As I continue to fall, the wind whistles in my ears. I am filled with the emotions of that day, we three friends, stood together in revenge against Adam Colwaite. I start laughing as I remember the walk home through the woods. For Jimmy, that was a defining moment in his life. When I next saw him he was unshackled and wanted to discover the world, our little world at least.

"Let's go scrumping," Jimmy said.

"Alright," said Simon.

"Where?" I asked.

"Crookballs Estate," replied Jimmy.

Crookballs Estate was at the other end of town and had a fabulous apple orchard. Every kid in town liked to try to scrump apples from Crookballs Estate, and every one of them had an adventure to tell you. They were rites of passage in our village, scrumping the apples and poaching the trout.

We headed up the high street, past the shops, and turned left at the church. The grounds to Crookballs

Estate were fenced off but there were a few places you could get in – the sort of places local wildlife, dogs and small kids knew about. We knew the best way was to walk right through the front gates. We had discovered this the year before during the summer. Every year, Crookballs held a pig roast, and all of the village would turn up to eat, drink and be merry. Simon and I had run off to play: unnoticed by the adults entertaining themselves we headed straight for the woods. It wasn't long before we found ourselves by the entrance of the estate, but still in the woods. The entrance road from the main gate was lined with woodland and as the road curved off to the right, no-one inside the main house could see the front gates. There was no more crawling through mud, using the animal entrances or hanging double your own height from a branch for us; after this discovery we always walked, proud as punch, through the main entrance and then simply darted off into the woods. The apple orchards were at the back of the house, so we would walk around the perimeter, staying in the woods, careful not to be seen. There were very few places to run to, and if you were caught you were in big trouble.

About halfway around, we could see the apple orchard and some staff walking across the lawn towards the front of the house. We continued a little further until we were at the back of the orchard. The trees were laid out in a formal manner in neat rows, and the safest way for us to get to the apples was for one of us to keep watch while the other two ran out of the woods to grab the apples from the lower branches. This was still a twenty-yard run. Jimmy and I were good runners, so Simon kept watch, a very important role and we gave Simon various instructions on how this was best done. After the plan was agreed we found Simon a good hiding place with a view from all angles. This was behind a bush on the edge of the woods, a spot we had used before. Jimmy and I braced ourselves and waited for the signal from Simon. Simon scanned the area and then nodded to Jimmy and I. Following the plan, Jimmy went first, and I followed. We scurried across the lawn towards the trees, grabbed a low branch, picked and plucked apples, dropping them into our pulled up t-shirts. Once we had more than we could possibly eat, we sprinted back. We headed back into the woods, sat down behind an old fallen tree and gorged ourselves on juicy apples. To young boys, scrumped apples have a taste of adventure that you can't find in a shop-bought apple. After we had finished our feat, Jimmy said he wanted to fish the river for some trout and pulled a hand line and some hooks from his pocket. I suspected Jimmy had a mind to do some poaching from the off, but wanted company and knew suggesting the raid on the apple orchard was a good way to get us in.

Fishing the river running through Crookballs Estate was forbidden, and the trout in this section of the river were specimens to be proud of. It was known to many locals that Mr Mumford, the housekeeper, enjoyed feeding these trout. Mr Mumford was a large man, to us children, a giant. He had hands like shovels and legs like tree trunks. He was one of those people who was as wide as he was tall, and had the bellowing voice to match. If he were an animal, Mr Mumford would have been a shire horse.

There was a section of the riverbank that had at some time been dug away to enlarge the river and made to look like a pond. This area was a little shallower and had a bridge which spanned the banks. We often poached fish, but this was the first time we had tried to poach Crookballs Estate. It was agreed we would stay on the wooded side of the river, and as Jimmy had only one line, the other two would keep watch. Simon found some fat, white grubs in one of the fallen trees, which Jimmy used to bait his hook. Jimmy cast out into the water and tugged on the line, trying to catch the attention of some fish. Again and again, he cast out the line, but was unable to catch anything. From our side of the bank, hiding behind the reeds, it was very difficult to see the fish, and it was awkward for Jimmy too, throwing the line over the top of the reeds. Very soon we all got bored and began offering our own suggestions of how to catch a fish. As each idea was discussed and dismissed, Jimmy slowly made his way to the bridge.

"Come and look at these beauties," he whispered to us.

Simon and I crawled onto the bridge, and what a sight we saw. We had heard about the trout in the river, but to see them jostling from side to side, the biggest ones maintaining their right to the best position, was hypnotising. Of course, as young, excited boys with limited concentration we soon snapped out of our trance and returned to arguing over the best method to catch a trout. Jimmy saw the trout he wanted and watched as its tail swayed from side to side majestically, guarding its swim. He put a fat grub onto his hook and tossed it into the water, gently tugging on the line, trying to manoeuvre it under the trout's nose. The grub was sinking too quickly and rolling along the bottom, bouncing and tumbling off the gravel bed. Jimmy was becoming impatient.

"Just hold the line so that the grub sits higher in the water," Simon suggested.

Jimmy threw the line back in and held it a little longer, and the grub started to rise. The three of us all leaned down on the bridge, tensing up with excitement as Jimmy steered the grub into the face of the trout. The trout moved to one side, spooked by the grub.

"Damn it," Jimmy said.

"Try a fresh one," I suggested.

Jimmy pulled in the line and took off the old, now dead grub and tossed it back into the river. As we watched the grub, a trout popped out from some weed and snatched it up.

"That's the one! I'll have that bugger," said Jimmy with a huge grin on his face.

With a new grub on his hook and a trout with a taste for the grub, Jimmy tossed the line back into the river, this time to the left of the other trout about a third of the way up from the patch of weed. The grub drifted past and the trout popped its head out. We all held our breath as it edged closer... another trout made a move across, spooking the one we were after.

"Damn it!" said Jimmy again.

"Damn it indeed," came a voice.

We all looked up and there stood the giant Mr Mumford.

"Damn it indeed," Mr Mumford said again.

We all leapt to our feet, but Mr Mumford was stood in front of us, blocking our way across the bridge, our exit to the woods. We froze. Mr Mumford was silent.

A fish took the line and pulled on Jimmy's hand. "I've got one! I've got one!" he screamed. He fell back to the floor and started reeling in the fish. Mr Mumford moved towards Jimmy, seeing an exit, Simon and I bolted across the bridge towards the woods, and my little adrenalin-fuelled legs zipped through the woods, everything a blur, bouncing up and down in front of me. My heightened senses picked out the low branch and I ducked, within five strides I jumped over a fallen tree, and what felt like seconds later I made it out of the woods, through the gates and across the road. I stopped to lean against a wall, breathing heavily; Simon who was only a few yards behind me collapsed onto the path, each of us wondering whether the other had seen Jimmy. We waited for a few minutes and discussed going back to look, got as far as the iron gates, and heard the siren. Simon and I jumped over a fence into the field opposite and headed back home.

On the walk home, panic and our imagination had us convinced that Jimmy had been arrested and was being interrogated by the police, and it wouldn't be long before they arrived at our houses to arrest us. We arrived on our street and waited on the corner, siting against a wall, discussing our worst fears; a good hiding from our parents; being taken away to a boys' home; our parents so ashamed they would never take us back... Simon wasn't sure his parents could take the stress. With all the boys in his house, one or two them had been arrested in the past, so it made sense to Simon that his parents would say he had to go away to learn his lesson. We promised each other if we ended up in the same boys' home we would stand by each other; we had heard the stories of how tough the boys could be. I told Simon I would plead with my parents not to let them send us away. I would reason we had never been in trouble before and it wouldn't happen again – we had learnt our lesson.

A red car came down the road and turned onto our street. Simon and I were crouched behind a parked car, trying to see who it was.

"It's Mumford," Simon whispered to me.

"What's he doing?" I asked.

"He's talking to Jimmy," Simon replied.

"Does he have handcuffs on?" I asked.

"No." Simon replied

"What's he doing then?" I asked again.

Simon looked at me. "I don't know!" he said, sternly.

"Bye Mr Mumford," We heard Jimmy shout.

"See you Saturday," Mr Mumford replied.

Mr Mumford drove off. Simon and I leapt from behind the car. "Jimmy! Jimmy!" we both shouted.

"Where's the police?" I asked.

"Are we in trouble?" Simon asked at the same time.

"Trouble? What police?" Jimmy replied. "Did you think the police were coming?" Jimmy had a smirk on his face.

"No. I didn't," Simon replied before I could.

Jimmy and Simon both looked at me.

"We did talk about it, Simon," I said, defending myself. "Not much though," I added "What's in the bag?" I changed the subject.

"My trout!" he replied.

Jimmy then told us how Mr Mumford had helped to pull the fish out. As he started to tell him off, he had been distracted by a bird call in the woods. Jimmy recognised it as a jay and told Mr Mumford as such.

Mr Mumford, a keen bird-watcher, was impressed and they got talking. Jimmy told him he had noticed it before, and that we had found an old nest the previous year while playing the woods. They followed the jay's call into the trees and found a new nest, not far from its previous home. After watching the jay for a bit, Mr Mumford offered to drive Jimmy home, let him keep the trout, wrote down a recipe for him, and offered him a Saturday job.

15ᵀᴴ FLOOR

Filled with happy memories from times spent with childhood friends, it is very easy to forget why I stepped off the building. This new sense of time I have seems to allow for some reflection as my life is appearing before my eyes and I have not yet hit the ground. Something stirs inside of me and I feel I am not alone. I have awoken something deep within me and I am starting to sense a new life, not death! The butterfly leaving the cocoon, but something is not quite right. I can hear myself screaming and I am aware I am falling through the air towards the ground.

"Please take me with you, don't let me die," a voice says. A desperate voice, my voice, but I am not talking. "Focus, please focus," the voice says. "You have to try and focus. The body will separate from the soul. You have to hold it together, then we won't die," the voice tells me. "Please don't let me die," the voice pleads.

This feeling I have awoken something, this sense of a new life, is not new but familiar. I am floating, all of the galaxies surround me. I can see the stars.

I can touch light beams as they pass by me. I hold my hands out to catch the light. I feel a tingling as it passes through my fingers and then my hand, leaving a yellow colour. A purple light passes through my leg, leaving a "purple" feeling where it passed. I start to see whole light spectrums and sense them too; I can feel them like moods, some uplifting and others depressing. I can mix any pallet of colours and make my own cocktails of emotions.

"Stop drifting away!" my voice shouts at me.

I am startled and confused by the voice, outside of my head and yet clearly mine. I don't understand what is happening to me.

"You do not have your memory yet; you have not been met. I am you, your ego," the voice tells me.

"What am I?" I ask.

"You are part of the soul; I need you to stop separating. Come back to me, come back to the body and I won't die," my ego says.

"Am I not in my body?" I reply.

"You are leaving; you just don't know it yet. Stay! And I can survive," my ego tells me.

"Leaving? Leaving where?" This question starts a process.

The muffled reply is background noise. I am aware that my ego is trying to tell me something, instructions I think. The noise soon becomes a distant sound. "How do you leave the body?" I think to myself. I have never given much thought to spiritual practices, my parents did not send me to church and I never heard them discuss God or religion. I remember seeing priests saying, "In the name of the father and of the son and of the holy spirit. Amen." I suppose this could be the new age Mind, Body, Spirit I have seen in magazines at the dentist. The ego, body and soul, I suppose. Without me, the ego dies, and the body can't live without the soul.

"Not always true," a voice tells me, a voice I don't recognise.

"Who's that? Who's there?" I ask.

No one replies and suddenly I feel a jolt. I can open my human eyes and I am falling towards the ground. Fear rages through my body. Time is back to how I knew it before I stepped off the roof, the world rushing past as gravity speeds up my fall towards the ground.

"You shouldn't have come back. Once you hear the voice there's no coming back," my ego tells me.

My vision starts to change and I see people surrounded by energy, the world in different layers, dimensions interlinked and crossing over each other.

"From the moment you are born I hide this from you. I take your memory. It's how the design works," my ego tells me. "I never thought you would step off the roof."

Another jolt goes through my body. It feels like I have been kicked hard in the stomach. As I recoil from the shock I start to separate. I can still see through the eyes of my body, the panic now subsiding. It becomes clear we are separate life forms, coexisting, and I have just evacuated instead of using my return ticket.

As this happens, I see the flesh, arteries, and my heart pumping blood at a tremendous rate. The separating brings confusion, who am I and how do I exist? This question becomes a thought wave and starts to travel. As I watch I too travel back to the universe of light beams and colours.

"You are you." An answer comes to me.

"The question is why did you come here and what have you learnt?"

I don't hear a voice or a sound, a thought, maybe, I think!

I try to speak as I would before. Instead, it becomes thought. "OK, why did I come here and what have I learnt?"

There is a bright light, which dims to sunlight. I am outside the building. I can see my body falling, but from the outside now. I am no longer coexisting. I stand, mid-air. I have no feelings of panic or fear; I have a sense I have done something wrong. I indulged in a moment of selfishness, my actions self-motivated with no perspective of the bigger design. I start to feel a tingle: I am changing into a colour similar to the light beams, and I hold out my hand and see a golden white light breaking through my skin. Bit by bit it spreads, my body disappears, and soon I am a form of light. I still have thoughts; I remember how old thoughts felt. Guilt has gone and I do not feel weighed down emotionally.

I feel weightless and free. Alive! Being dead feels great! I once only saw physical bodies, animals with hair, feathers, trees and bark. They are all transparent shells now, with an energy resonating from inside. Each identical to its species, everything is just energy: trees look like other trees; dogs all look alike, cats, birds – they all look like their own kind. Only humans are the exception. Some of us are bright, especially the ones laughing or in love. The solemn ones are a dull glow, like an old light bulb.

14TH FLOOR

head down to the ground. I have to explore this new freedom. I stop just above the pavement, across from the couple who are arguing. These two are very different people. She has a pink glow to her golden light, and from inside I see a second smaller glow. She is pregnant. To say "I see" is not really accurate, more that sound and sight are also now feelings and emotion. All my senses combine into one, a knowing, so I know, feel, sense, experience that she is pregnant, that there is the light of a new soul inside of her. Her partner, no it's her lover, it was her lover! The emotions are still mixed and reading them I feel how confused she is. His light is cloudy and charged with negative thoughts, he chases after her, shouting.

"Angie, wait, I am sorry, please give me a chance! It's different than before – we could have a family together! I'm a dad!"

She stops.

From Gary's light, energy tries to surround Angie and suppress her own light. Angie's light acts like a suit of armour, trying its hardest to reflect Gary's energy away. They are not aware of what is happening. This is their subconscious, controlling the energy inside. Angie is trying to defend herself to escape but he is very strong-willed and unwilling to let her go. As Gary puts his arms around Angie she shrugs them off.

"Stop, I've had enough, I don't want this anymore," Angie tells Gary.

"Angie what about the baby... I had no father."

This sends a shockwave through Angie's energy; her thoughts have turned to guilt, her armour now fades, the light shield once protecting her flickers, weakens and starts to shrink inside of her. Gary puts his arm around her again and Angie doesn't resist. As he does so I see his energy wrap around her like a boa constrictor, binding her tight, suffocating her. As I look at Gary I feel his thoughts, "She's mine. She's mine." This thought strengthens his energy: he turns and smiles at Angie.

"You know I love you, don't you?" Gary asks Angie.

Gary doesn't know love. His own negative thoughts have smothered his light to just the slightest glow. His energy surrounds Angie, and as she tries to think for herself, his energy feeds on hers. He has made Angie very weak. Angie's light is still strong, even now, but her will is all but destroyed and Gary knows this. Not on a conscious level; Gary believes he has just convinced his girl to come back to him. His ego knows better.

It has control and it feels good, powerful. He will feed off Angie whenever the world is not working for him: a bad day at work will be Angie's fault, and when the baby has ruined his life that will be Angie's fault too. Gary's ego has found another ego to take the blame, so nothing will now be his fault or his responsibility. As I watch this, I experience an insight I never knew was possible. I am detached from any pain I would have expected to feel. Still, I do not like what I am seeing and I sense this will not be a great life for Angie or the baby. I move towards Angie and Gary's energy moves towards me, putting up a barrier. I step through this and it tries to surround me. I combine with her body and this coexisting feels limited and restrictive. I hear the blood whooshing as the heart beats, and noises on the street from through her ears. The senses feel individual again but I am still divided; it's not a real coexistence. I feel a surge of energy inside Angie's body as her inner strength regains momentum. Her energy is feeding off mine; Angie's light is recharging from my energy. This is not parasitic like Gary's, stealing energy that does not belong to him, feeding himself to make Angie weak. This is nurturing, a reminder to Angie's soul of its existence, helping her to rejuvenate, to replenish her light so that she can shine brightly and independently once again. I feel Angie's rage and love for Gary. She is confused and so am I. As I take on this confusion, future events appear in my mind and

I see Angie and Gary arguing, Angie packing a bag, Gary charging into the room and punching her to the floor. The intensity shocks me, and Angie sees what I am seeing.

"No, I can't," Angie tells Gary.

"Arrgh, stop! You're so stupid!" Gary replies, and grabs Angie's arm.

Angie flinches and I feel her fear, just like I used to feel when I saw Adam Colwaite. It is just a coincidence, but as the memories flood back from that day in the woods, my emotions combine with Angie's.

"Angie this is your last chance," Gary tells her.

Angie and I grab Gary by the throat, and I feel her finger tips squeezing his neck as Angie interrupts his next line. My single thought brings a strength no individual could harness.

We lift Gary off the floor and slam him into a wall, the back of his head cracking open with the impact. As Angie looks into his eyes, I stare through his eyes and find his ego, now a quivering child. I focus my thought and this energy moves into Gary's consciousness. I become the dark clouds surrounding Gary's ego as it begs for mercy not to be hurt. This negative force which fed on Angie is all but swallowed up by my rage. Angie lets go of Gary's throat and as she does she severs my connection with Gary's ego. Angie runs down the road, her strength not only returned but stronger, with a greater sense of self-worth. Angie runs into a park, slows down and sits on a bench. Holding her head in her hands she ponders what to do next, and as she does the answer comes to us. She has an aunt. Angie sits upright; "I will stay with my aunt," she thinks to herself. Angie gets up, and as she leaves I stay behind, sitting on the bench. Within seconds I am back to being nothing but energy and light.

13TH FLOOR

I have 360-degree awareness, none of the limitations of a human body, and as I watch Angie walk away I feel a sense of love. Her light has a gold centre, a yellow surround and a pink outer glow. This love I sense seems to be a natural state, not like when you fall in love, more a paternal love, or the love you see in an elderly couple's eyes. An everlasting love. I feel it for myself first and this seems to reflect to all around me. I have a desire to share this and look around to see if I can help anyone else, anyone I can combine with to replenish their energy. The local shopping centre will be full of people and as I think of going there, I arrive. I see the crowds pushing past each other as they walk from shop to shop. I can tune into the energies of everyone, and sense those emitting a lower energy than they are capable of. I am surprised by how many this is. Next to me is an elderly gentleman, and I sense his loneliness: he misses his wife. I wonder what he misses and as I move to combine with him I feel reluctance. As I wonder how to help him an orb of energy leaves me and settles into his core, slowly his energy changes and a tear falls down his cheek. He brushes this off, gets up and walks away. To his side I notice a blur, I focus and then see the energy next to him. His wife by his side, a very different energy to mine, she is almost transparent. I now understand why I could not combine with her husband.

I have a sense of higher levels of consciousness.

I look around again, and inside the coffee shop I watch people drinking their coffee just like I have myself before, eavesdropping on conversations. Now I am aware that their feelings are different to their words. Despite many fluctuations in energies, I feel nothing as intense as I did with Angie and Gary. There is nothing of real interest: everyone seems to be where they choose to be. I look at a boy on a children's car ride, laughing as he rocks backwards and forwards pressing the horn. I start to feel giddy from his joy and he is becoming blurred. The ride stops and this upsets the boy; instantly I snap out of my giddiness. I find myself right next to him absorbing his energy, now distraught. I never realised just how much joy a child could hold inside, nor how upsetting the loss of such a simple thing can be. The boy, Jacob is his name, is now being dragged through the shopping centre by his arm, crying and pro-testing to his mother. She is too preoccupied with her time to understand how happy Jacob was, and Jacob is fortunately still too young to be preoccupied by time.

I feel someone on the third floor and find a young woman called Sarah, staring at herself in the mirror. She is hating everything she sees. She grabs at flesh at her waist, pulls at her hair, internally condemning herself, so much emphasis on herself, her perception of ugliness. Encouraging all of this I see her ego, supporting her emotions, encouraging her imagination. I think of the joy from Jacob and start to single thought my way into Sarah's energy as I did with Angie.

"STOP!" someone shouts at me.

I'm startled, but see no-one. I imagine it must be a trick of the ego and start again.

"I SAID STOP!" I hear, and again seeing no-one I continue towards Sarah. As I do I am sent reeling backwards, shunted out of my single thought. I see Sarah standing in front of the mirror and between us, a blur. Slowly, I focus, and in front of me stands a homeless woman, a tramp. Confused, I step forward again, trying to bypass the tramp. She whacks me across the chest and sends me reeling back for a second time. The tramp marches towards me; I try and maintain focus to think my way out of here. As I do I see my ideas of places to manifest swirling around my head, every thought increasing my confusion. I am starting to panic.

Everything slows and the confusion swirling around me dissipates. My awareness returns. I am surrounded by darkness. I am in the night sky. I do not know where I am but I can see stars twinkling, I try to recognise any of the constellations, but these are new to me. A light appears in front of me like a tear in the fabric of the sky, and as it opens, the tramp walks through. I try to flee but I hit an invisible wall. I turn to face the tramp and try to grab her, she hits me with some sort of light and I am knocked over. Winded, I see her walk over to me.

"Who gave you responsibility for Sarah?" she asks.

"I... I... I..." I stutter, unable to answer.

"A jumper. You have a split second outside of your body and you try to fix the world. You should have tried fixing it when you were there!" the tramp sneers.

"Who are you?" I ask.

"You can stay here with the others," she replies.

The tramp walks away and I am in a park sitting on a park bench. Not a park I am familiar with, but as with most parks, they all look the same. Wide open space, mowed lawns and trees, the sky is blue and judging from the sun it looks to be midday. I stand up and look around. A few hundred yards away I see the tramp also sitting on a bench. She glances over and then turns away. I see others, some sleeping on the grass, reading books, a guy doing Tai Chi... it really is like any other park I have visited. I walk over to another bench and sit myself down, ask myself where I am, but unlike before, I receive no answers. I think this must be a holding place, a collecting point, a cross-over stage. I am hoping these thoughts will prompt answers. I think about the girl, Sarah, from the shopping mall. What happened and how did I end up here? Again nothing comes to me. Now I am feeling disconnected. I try to focus my thoughts, a single thought, the building I stepped off... slowly I feel something manifesting within me. I breathe in and slowly breathe out; I start to feel a tingling. Suddenly I am grabbed by the throat and lifted into the air.

"I am not a saint and do not have the patience of one. Control your thoughts or I will control them for you," the tramp says, and then let's go of me. I fall to the floor. This feels just like being on earth in my body! I gag and rub my throat. I am feeling fear again. I certainly don't like this place. The tramp is standing next to me and through her legs I see a man walking over.

"Alright, mate?" he says.

He looks at the tramp and she walks away.

"No I'm not alright!" I reply.

"Don't worry," he says and then chuckles. "Don't worry; I forget we can't worry, not here anyway. Have you tried to worry? It doesn't work!" he tells me.

"I was pretty worried then!" I reply.

"I'm Darren." He holds out his hand and helps me to my feet.

"I'm..."

"Michael, I know," he says interrupting me. "Still feeling worried?" Darren asks.

I'm not; I'm feeling a connection again.

"No," I reply to Darren.

"You shouldn't – not here anyway. The pastor must have thought it for you. They can do that sort of thing," Darren says.

"Who's the pastor?" I ask.

"I see a pastor; he looks like my uncle Jim. What do you see?" Darren asks.

"I see a tramp and a lady," I reply. "What is she?"

"Ummm, they're kind of guardians, light warriors or something. It's still a bit hazy," Darren says.

"Angels?" I suggest.

"No, I've never seen one of them. They do exist though, just not here. We all see things differently: I see a pastor and you see a tramp. It's something to do with our perception and limitations. There is only so much we can understand as we're still on earth, we're not really souls. The tramp, she is a soul – they have much more understanding and ability, but none of us know what they really look like. The ones that watch over us are older, much older. They all have their own specialities and jobs, they don't reincarnate anymore, and they stay up here. Sometimes dark energies appear and they go off to fight, but they always come back so they must win..."

"And this place? What is this?" I ask.

"I call it Limbo Park. Everyone you see, all alive back on earth, waiting for their body to die. I'll show you," Darren says.

I'm standing in a hospital room, and Darren's body is lying on the bed, wired up to a machine. The woman next to him is his wife. I feel connected again and knew this as soon as I glanced at her.

"She comes every day, hoping I'll wake up. Never gonna happen. That body is mangled, but until they switch off the machine the ego won't let me go."

"Is that what happens when we die – we move on?" I ask.

"If you die of natural causes, it was just your time, then friends and family will be waiting. People you knew and soul-mates, the ones you knew before you incarnated: they'll meet you. But us, our deaths weren't part of the soul's plan. They didn't ready themselves for the connection to be severed and..." Darren pauses. "And we intended it to happen; we wanted this."

Darren changes our perception and I am standing in a kitchen. Darren walks in with a glass in his hand. He pulls out a bottle of vodka from a cupboard, pours some into the glass and knocks it back. He opens a drawer and pulls out a bottle of tablets, pours another vodka and pops the pills in his mouth and knocks back the vodka. He grabs some keys and walks out of the kitchen.

"Oh boy, did those pills make me drowsy. The drinking I would have gotten away with," Darren tells me.

"And you?" As Darren says this I see the wall of the building in front of me and as we look up I am stepping off the building.

"Whoop whoop!" Darren yells. "We have a quickie. Not long for you at all, they'll bounce you straight back. That's what happens with jumpers you disconnect real quick."

"I'm going back?" I ask.

"Yep! When you jump, land, crash, OD whatever; if you are the cause of your own downfall they bounce you back!" Darren throws his arms in the air. "You live again!"

I stand silently. I'm not shocked or worried. Darren was right, those emotions are not possible. I cannot even be concerned; I am left with the feeling, "what was the point?"

"It's not that bad, Michael, they re-jig a few things. A new set of circumstances, a complete new life, you get to try again," Darren tells me.

"How do you know so much?"

"I've been in that coma for seven months. The doctors know I won't return, my wife knows and slowly, every day, my ego lets go of a little bit more. As it does, the knowledge starts to return."

I think about the prospect of going back down. On Earth if you spoke of death and you were "going down" it meant you were going to hell. Maybe it is the same up here. I say "up here", I do not know where "here" is, if it's up or down. I look at Darren, thinking about his circumstances, and the answers arrive. He's married, he found out his wife was having an affair. He had a couple of drinks, took some pills and went for a drive. He intended to find a place to stay. While he drove around he went over and over what his wife had done, anger set in and he decided to drive into a tree. His wife sits there every day praying he will come back to her. She doesn't know he knew about the affair and the guilt is ripping her apart. Darren knows this, and every day he visits her too, until he can't bear the pain any longer, so he returns to Limbo Park.

"The knowledge is not always good, my friend," Darren says.

And he is right. Darren visits his wife every day, knowing he is helpless to intervene. Being attached to the body, he still feels the love for his wife, and he feels her suffering. Like I helped Angie, Darren takes his on his wife's pain.

"I tried to make her switch off the machine, but the pastor stops me. If I can take away her suffering, maybe she will listen to the doctors and switch off the machine. I wouldn't see her again, I would forget, I would be born again..." Darren walks away and fades out of sight. He has gone to visit his wife again. I can feel him pleading with her.

12ᵀᴴ FLOOR

As I ponder Darren and how he wishes his wife would turn off his life support, my insight tells me this is a lesson for Darren. I feel Darren wants to return to Earth so the suffering will end. No more watching his wife, feeling the hurt and guilt, experiencing his wife's emotions on such an intense level. Feeling love is great: it can be overwhelming in a wonderful way, the emotional freedom quite literally heavenly. I have experienced human emotions for myself in my current state and I know how this hurts. The intensity weighs you down, it can make you feel human again, unlike Jacob's joy which was special. I am fortunate to have experienced two people I have no connection to, and no-one I loved as a human, but unlike Darren I have no desire to go back. Darren called me a "quickie" a reference that I would bounce straight back into another body. I had not given any thought to this. I left for a reason and those reasons are still the same. There was no dramatic event, it was just weariness over time, and I decided I had had enough. I wanted to leave.

I did not know what leaving was or where I was going. It could very well have been the last thing I would do. I didn't seek any guarantees. It was my decision and one I reinforced with certainty every moment from when I got up this morning. My time was over and I stepped off the edge. Now I am in Limbo Park, waiting for the next moment to happen, whatever the next moment may be. I think about my son, James. I gaze across the park and look to the horizon and wonder what he is doing. He is in his flat. I look around. I cannot see the tramp. It is time for me to move on, and as quick as that I am standing outside the door of James's flat. I lift my hand to ring the doorbell. I stop. What am I going to say? Will he see me?

I laugh to myself. I am amused I even thought I should ring the doorbell. If I can manifest my way here, why knock? I may as well surprise him – at least that will enable me to tell him I am dead. Well, not quite dead yet – I am still falling – but I will be dead. I could just arrive in his kitchen. He would be shocked and I could then disappear and manifest to another room. That should enable me to break the ice. How do I tell him I am dead?

I hear the lift doors open and James walks out. He heads towards his door, where I am standing, but does not notice me. He pulls the keys out of his pocket and opens the door. He pauses and makes that movement we all make when we feel that shiver, as if, as the saying goes, "someone has just walked over my grave". Not quite, but close, in this case. Another thing I haven't thought out, and now I feel I want to talk to James. I seek out Darren for help and answers.

"Hello Darren." Darren is standing at his hospital bedside. He doesn't reply.

"Darren, sorry to intrude I have some questions." Again, Darren doesn't answer.

I wave and stand in front of Darren, calling out his name. Nothing. He can't see me either. I ask myself why, but no answer comes. I take a deep breath, let it all out and focus my senses, and I feel nothing. I silent my mind and take myself into the cosmos, the dark backdrop amongst bright stars. I have nothing, and as I dwell I have an old feeling, a niggling in my mind. I am feeling a sense of guilt, not strong, related to James. I distract myself and think of James, where he is, and instantly I can see this. I do the same for Darren and, again, instantly I see him. I ask myself again how to talk with Darren and I get nothing. The guilt is there again, a little stronger this time. I manifest myself to the bench in Limbo Park. I see the tramp sitting on a bench. As I walk over to her the scenery changes; with every step the pristine lawns of Limbo Park change to long grasses and wild flowers. I glance behind and the pristine lawns are there. Now as I look at the tramp she is sitting on a log, not a bench, the pond I sat beside in the park now a rugged, wild lake.

"Take a seat," the tramp tells me.

I sit down, and across the lake I see woods and behind the woods, mountains. I look back to my park bench and it is still a pristine lawn. As I follow the bank of the lake I can see some paving as it turns into a typical pond found in any city park.

"We all have heavens, here it is limitless. I like this view and the park suits your idea of heaven. As you move around you cross into different energies, heavens," the tramp tells me.

"Makes sense," I reply, agreeing more than understanding. The tramp looks at me. She knows I don't really understand.

"Forms, options, space... there are no limits. Everyone has what they want. Every soul in Heaven could fit on this log and see a different view. Everyone has an individual perception."

"Perception becomes thought manifestation, thought manifestation becomes reality," I say to the tramp.

As I say this I see the pristine, well-kept park all around me.

"Very good, instant answers," she says to me.

I notice a field of energy surrounding the tramp for the first time, and I can seamlessly switch between the two. Within seconds I no longer notice the energy field, but I feel a new awareness based on thoughts alone.

"You're becoming energy again, a soul without the body, but you are still connected to a physical form. It is limited and limits your possibilities of perception. What you are experiencing now is more of a lucid dream or an out-of-body experience," the tramp explains.

"I think I understand..." I reply. "What is it like, what are you really?"

The tramp smiles "That's a big one," she replies. "Right now you are a physical falling body with a soul; this is a human term and in no way holds a candle to the reality, which actually isn't a reality. Everything is nothing more than a thought from one consciousness manifested and continually expanding. It encompasses matter, space, dimensions and perceptions. A single source of consciousness is responsible for all that ever will be and it knows no limits. We are all part of this at various different levels of manifestation and perception and right now in your human terms you are asking me to help you understand how to create, build and run a nuclear power station when you're still studying to try and pass the 'How to Change a Light Bulb' exam."

"Oh," I reply.

"Oh indeed, but don't worry, you get to go back and try to pass the light bulb exam again," she says, half joking. "If you want, you have time to visit James, but he won't be able to see you."

I look at the tramp. I'm no longer fearful, admiring her view, smiling at what she sees. She is wearing an old, tall hat which is crumpled with some holes, her large winter overcoat is threadbare and torn in places. She wears an ancient red and white checked scarf, which as I look is actually an old shirt which has been torn into the shape of a scarf. Everything about her look is clichéd and stereotyped, almost a Charles Dickens' character.

"If you think you can do a better tramp, you have a go!" she challenges me.

"You could teach me a few tricks. I quite fancy a sea view for my place!" I reply.

The tramp stands up and brushes herself down.

"I thought about ignoring you when we first met, just letting you interfere. Your intentions were good, so no harm could really come from it, but as you fall closer to earth you will have realisation followed by guilt and this weighs heavy," she tells me.

"But I'm OK because I'm here," I tell her.

"You're OK because you haven't hit the floor yet," the tramp replies, her voice stern. "And you may not want to go back, but souls do not carry guilt. Guilt is a physical attribute and when you impact you will be severed from the body and be truly free. In that moment your life will stand before you like a mirror and if you do not like your reflection you will feel guilt. Your only perception of life is a confused God's image, divine love, unconditional in a way that is impossible for you to grasp. You will judge yourself by this, not with kindness but with a greater perception of reality from the consciousness. Without a normal transition you cannot let go of the perception, and guilt is so heavy it requires a physical body to hold it."

"So I need to learn how to forgive myself?" I ask.

"Follow me, I'll show you those learning to forgive themselves," the tramp says.

As I follow the tramp we become surrounded by darkness. "Stay close," she tells me.

As the darkness encroaches I feel a substance in the air. I am being checked out. The darkness feels like an emotion, heavy, but different from my old friend Mr Grey. We continue forward and I can hear faint cries in the distance. As we get closer, I hear people moaning and crying, some sobbing their hearts out. I don't see anyone and the dark feels thick as if I am moving through something. I have lost all feeling of freedom and joy, there is a weight inside my midriff, and for the first time I feel the floor beneath me. It is cold, wet, and with a black sticky substance. It is seeping into the soles of my feet, moving past my ankles. As it enters my veins, my heart starts to pump again. Am I human? I don't feel like energy. The substance is pulling me to the floor and the poison in my veins is transforming me into an emotional wreck; every guilt, fear and torment I have ever known is multiplied and it's all my fault. I failed as a child, and as an adult. I could have achieved so much more. I had chances, I ignored the possibilities. I collapse to the floor.

The tramp grabs me and lifts me up. I am slumped over her shoulder, sobbing, struggling to breathe. I am weak. The tramp plunges a sword into my body and I gasp air, my body fills with light. Within seconds I am energised; literally I am energy again, back to feeling my soul-self. The tramp puts me down and from the light emitting from her sword I can see lost souls lying on the floor; some sobbing others motionless all of them poisoned by the black substance. I can see movement; it is faint but there is something out there in the darkness. They are energy forms of guilt, feeding off the lost souls. On the physical plane I would know them as demonic energies, feeding off the souls, keeping them imprisoned, an extended and frightening version of the egos I saw in people when I first stepped off the roof. They are from various lifetimes, not all suicides, but they all suffered on Earth with their guilt and carried this over. The demons are tortured souls who experienced divine acceptance, their place in the greater part of our universe, the existence of all things. No, that's not it, I have these answers but they are so limited and it comes through in a language I do not understand. Somehow these souls plunge into turmoil and do not leave the body, or they get here and it's not what they expected, or they can't understand the process so they don't reconnect. Maybe it's all of these things.

"They don't have to stay," the tramp tells me.

The tramp is no longer in her dirty ragged clothes, or even looking human. She is a pure energy, radiating light.

"Are you a god?" I ask, feeling a little silly.

"No, I'm a tramp," she replies in a tedious tone.

Her light dims slightly and I see her face. She is dressed in armour with symbols and written engravings. She is holding a sword and stands proud before me, just like the stories of King Arthur I read as a child, getting ready to charge into battle. I feel I should bow down onto my knees.

"Get a grip of your thoughts. I am not a god, an angel or King Arthur. I am a realised soul, with no connection to physical planes. I am not worshipped, never have been and never will be. Only humans require forms of worship."

"Is this where I am going?" I ask her.

The tramp pauses. "Everything comes here in some form. It's where you let things go. If you were able to sit in Limbo Park and let it all go and drain into the lake, this is where the drain would overflow. Just like in physical life, whatever you can't let go of anchors you, and you never move forward. When you die the soul makes preparations, even at short notice. In suicide, it's a conflict with your ego, and that has no place here. It's your choice. We can prepare you to go back to Earth, live a new life. Or, when your body hits the ground, the connection will be severed and you will no longer live an out-of-body experience. There will be no light to follow." She raises her sword and opens a portal.

"Wait," she says.

Pointing her sword into the darkness, a bright orb appears from the end and moves away from us until it is a faint glow. In the depths of despair there is movement: the orb stops above a demon feeding off a soul, gorging itself on pain and, in doing so, forever holding the soul in an endless nightmare. This would indeed be hell!

"Help!" the soul calls out.

The orb brightens, forcing the demon to look up. The tramp heads towards the soul, the demon stands up, snarls and postures. It is translucent, hollow eyes and a body made up of souls, each soul relaying their life in what I can only describe as a charcoal coloured cartoon, their horrors on a continuous loop. Despite standing much taller than the tramp, it is cautious and does not move. It fears her.

"Do not interfere with our world. This one belongs here. She is still very tasty," the demon snarls.

"All souls who ask shall be reclaimed," the tramp replies.

"She's mine!" the demon screams.

The tramp continues towards the soul. The demon changes shape, drops onto all fours and charges towards the tramp. I cover my ears to protect me from the sound of a thousand souls screaming. The tramp stands her ground, looks back at me; a triangle shaped portal opens and I am pulled in away from any danger, but able to watch from the other side. The demon leaps forward and the tramp strikes with her sword, forcing the demon back, snarling and hissing. It lashes out, and as its talons strike the tramp a shield lights up, deflecting the blow. The tramp lunges forward, plunging her sword into its midriff. As it hits the translucent body the sword glows brightly; another strike hits its thigh and again forces the demon back, hissing and dragging its leg. The orb above the tramp becomes brighter again, grows around the soul lying on the floor. I see other, smaller demons who have watched the fight, and they start to circle their injured counterpart. As one steps forward, two from its flank attack, another comes charging out of the darkness. The demon is now fighting four smaller ones. They have it on its back, but despite its injury it is still stronger and fighting back. One of them mistakenly lunges in and feels some talons open its throat. The demon is finding a footing and gets back on all fours. It quickly pins another of its attackers down and bites hold swinging its head back and forth. The other two attackers retreat and disappear into the darkness. As the demon begins to feast on the bodies of its foes, I see the convergence of their souls. With every bite the demon takes, its wounds heal and it grows in size.

The tramp doesn't seem to notice, and ignores all that is going on. She has helped the lost soul to her knees and is helping her to drink. She then picks her up and walks towards the portal. The demon looks back at the tramp, but makes no challenge, content to feed on its own kind. As I walk down the portal I see guides coming towards me, they pass and go through to the domain of the demons. I watch as they send out orbs and light the darkness waiting to hear a call from a soul ready to move on. The demons wait and listen also, standing guard over their food.

11ᵀᴴ FLOOR

The tramp and the woman are sitting on a bench out-side of a church. As I look at the tramp, I see the overlay of a priest. The woman's name is Elaine. Her skin is pale, she has long hair and looks in her early thirties.

"Is she alright?" I ask the tramp.

"She just needs a moment."

"What did she do?" I enquire.

"Nothing."

"I sinned," Elaine says quietly.

The tramp takes her hand. "Come child, it's alright now."

"It kept coming back and hurting me. Every bite, I saw my mother when..." Elaine starts to sob. "I was only a child."

"It's time now, let's go inside," the tramp tells Elaine.

"God won't take me," Elaine says.

"God takes all who ask," the tramp replies. "Please take my hand and let me show you."

Elaine, still a little weak, stands up and follows the tramp into the church. The church has a familiarity about it, an old stone building, large wooden door, stained glass windows, and pews on either side and Jesus Christ on the cross above the altar. The tramp walks Elaine to the altar and helps her to kneel down. She lights two candles, one on either side of the altar and kneels next to Elaine, and they start to pray.

In my time in limbo I have not felt a need to come to church, or had a sense that I should. I am unable to sense why this is happening, and I know we are somewhere different to Limbo Park. The door of the church opens and a choir walk in, taking their place behind the altar. They start to sing All Creatures of our God and King. Having never been to church, I am unsure why this hymn has a familiar sound. As they sing I feel a powerful presence of energy, and a tall white body of light. An angel comes towards me and sits down by my side. Soon the church is filled with angels. They all have an outer glow, with slight colour variations. Sitting next to an angel I feel an intense, joyful love. I think of my son, James, and how, when I first held him, I felt a mixture of love, pride, awe and what can only be described as a gooey feeling inside, all wrapped up and bursting outwards, created by my feelings for my son. My body starts to tingle, and tears are flowing.

"They enhance feelings of love," the tramp says.

I can only nod in agreement as I wipe a tear of joy away. The choir start another hymn Lead Us, Heavenly Father, Lead Us. I look up at the angel sitting next to me. Unable to help myself, I raise my finger and touch the angel. I feel its energy, much greater than anything I have experienced. Even the tramp's energy doesn't come close, and I start to understand that an angel is the highest form of a soul. Soon, my hand starts to stroke the angel's face. I begin petting the angel like an excited child at the zoo. I have forgotten who and where I am. I am tapped on the shoulder quite hard. Startled, I look around to see the tramp, raising her eyes to Heaven and shaking her head. I become aware of myself again and I am kneeling on the bench almost on top of the angel. Embarrassed I sit back down and face the altar. Elaine is still kneeling, the choir start another song, and this time I listen.

O perfect love, All human thought transcending
Lowly we kneel in prayer before thy throne
That theirs may be the love which knows no ending
Whom thou forever more dost join in one

As the hymn continues I am drawn back to the angel. With head down low, I squint through the corner of my eye, trying to be discreet. I sit on my hands, trying hard to resist. I am helpless: my head is lifting and I am staring again. The angel turns its head to look at me or at least, the head is facing forward and turns in my direction. Staring directly into its eyes, I can see the universe, the stars, nebula clouds, life on worlds beginning... They all seem to be physical and then they blend into a conscious stream of energies, like busy highways lit up at night, the city somewhere in the distance. All energy, flowing from the one source. The angel blinks and pulls its energy away, looks at me smiling, and speaks to me. I cannot hear any words. A golden light appears in the centre of my body and streams of light peel away, filling my entire energy system and then dispersing.

"An angel blessing. Aren't you the lucky one!" the tramp comments.

Startled once again, I look around. The angels have gone, so has the church, and I am back in Limbo Park.

"That was intense," I tell the tramp. "What were her sins?" I cannot help but ask.

"Her sins? There are no sins, just reality and perception," the tramp shrugs.

"She wouldn't go into a perceived church, she was scared," I reply.

The tramp pokes me in the head.

"There is just reality, and she shed some preconceived ideas. This here, right now is your reality, not hers, not mine just yours. Every single person that has ever existed, does exist and will exist has their own reality."

She pokes my head again and continues.

"But you wrap yourselves up in an illusion, your everyday teaching teaches an illusion from the moment you take a physical matter form."

Again she pokes my head.

"So-called knowledge. You believe in the afterlife, but call it death. You want to go to Heaven, but you fear death and you teach people to be afraid. Everyone is going to die, but the soul carries on. But it will be judged, although by whom you can't all agree nor what is expected of you in order to pass that judgement. You teach this knowledge," the tramp says.

"Of course, knowledge can only be equal to your level of understanding," says a female voice.

I turn around. It is Elaine.

"Hi!" she says waving.

She looks very different. Her skin has colour, the sunken eyes are full and sparkle. She is wearing a floral dress. She looks alive, with a green outer ring.

"That was quick! What are you doing here?" I ask.

"Different places take different times. I have come to see you, I have a job and you can come with me," she says.

"Is that OK?" I ask the tramp.

"Who are you speaking to?" Elaine asks.

And just like that I am standing on the edge of a road, a dead end on an industrial estate. I see the headlights of a car, and as it approaches, I see a woman. Elaine, as a human, walks to the side of the pavement. The car stops and Elaine gets in. After a brief discussion, Elaine leans into his lap and disappears.

"You've seen enough," Elaine says.

"You got in the car, you were a..." I pause and don't finish.

"A prostitute," Elaine finishes.

"Sorry. I didn't mean anything by it."

"It's alright, on this physical plane I was a prostitute, in her reality I am, still am. They were right: half souls really are quite limited," Elaine says smirking.

We walk past some factories, leaving the industrial estate, and carry on down the main road. Elaine points to the bars and coffee shops she used to visit, telling me a little about some of the people she knew. We turn off the main road and down a side street, both sides lined with terraced houses. We stop outside number 43 and watch as Elaine walks up towards the door. She pauses and shudders, that tingling feeling down your spine again. She knocks on the door, and is greeted by someone called Andy. She is invited in. Elaine and I follow her into the sitting room. It's a nice room. It has a cosy feeling, brown leather sofa, natural wooden floors, a chunky rug and a wooden coffee table for a centrepiece. Above a Victorian fireplace sits the latest flat screen TV.

"Do you want a cuppa?" Andy asks.

"No thanks, just some gear."

"No worries," Andy replies. He takes a box off the shelf, opens it up and places a wrap on the table.

"If you don't have any cash, I'm in need of some," Andy tells her, and rubs his crotch.

"I've just had my last customer of the night. Thanks anyway," Elaine replies and puts some money on the table, takes the wrap and lights up a cigarette.

"I'm off. Thanks for the gear," Elaine says, and gets up to leave.

"Any chance of a change of mind? Stay the night, build up some credit?" Andy asks.

Elaine smiles. "Sweetheart, I need to go home. If you're feeling lonely on Monday let me know."

Elaine leaves the house and walks to the bus stop. We wait with her and when the bus arrives we sit a couple of seats behind her. There is a group of lads sitting at the back and Elaine looks back.

"Is everything alright?" I ask.

"It will be," Elaine replies.

One of them walks down the bus towards us, and as he does, Elaine sticks out her leg and trips him up.

"What did you do that for?" I ask.

"He wasn't going to be nice to me," she said with a smile on her face.

"Are you allowed to do that?" I enquire.

Elaine shrugs her shoulders and is still smiling. The lad on the floor picks himself up. His friends at the back of the bus are laughing. His nose is bleeding and he seems pretty dazed.

Elaine fist-pumps in the air. "Yes!" I look at Elaine astounded. "Don't worry, no one will care," she tells me. "Come on we're getting off soon."

"What are we doing?" I ask.

"I'm watching, reviewing parts of my life," Elaine answers. "If you look at me on a physical level I look disinterested, my skin scabby, but when you look at my energy, do you see the dark spots which float in my aura? These are karmic spots, not mine, others', events that happened before I reincarnated."

"Karmic spots? I thought karma was "what goes around comes around"?" I reply.

"In some ways it is, but on a larger scale. You can carry them through many incarnations."

"So are these markers of people you have wronged?" I ask.

"Not all of them. The ones that matter are from people I should have helped, that I agreed to help before I incarnated. It is not always because you wrong people, sometimes we are supposed to wrong. It may steer them in the right direction."

The bus stops and Elaine gets off. We follow Elaine into an apartment block, and get the lift to the eighth floor. As we are going up in the lift, physical Elaine is staring into the mirror and then looks around the lift. I can see she senses she is not alone. I can also see her conscious blocking her, preventing her from seeing us. We walk into the apartment. Elaine takes off her jacket, sits down and pulls the wrap out of her handbag. She lifts the lid off a box on the table and pulls out a spoon. She opens the wrap and puts some powder on the spoon, mixes it and takes some up in her syringe. Elaine ties her arm off, pumps up a vein and injects the solution into her arm. She sits back in her armchair and closes her eyes. I can see the fluid mixing in her blood, the chemicals reacting with the blood cells, moving up to the brain. The stimulus creates quite a light show as the high engages her ego.

Suddenly, Elaine gasps. Her heart is slowing, the pumping of blood winds down to a halt and the heart stops. I see, a few seconds before she is about to depart, her ego is clawing on the inside of her head, panic-stricken trying to grab hold of the soul as it starts its departure. A majestic white energy floats from the body upwards, never looking back. As it leaves, the ego slumps back, and like the rest of the body, becomes lifeless.

"Suicide?" I ask.

"No, a weak heart," Elaine replies. "I wasn't ready to go just yet, but I steered events this way. I'll show you."

We are standing in a café. It's 1963. I see a man and a woman on either side of a table, sharing a cup of tea.

"Don't worry, love, I know money is short, but we'll be fine," the man says. He kisses her hand, she smiles back, and I can see the love in her eyes. "I'm seeing Malcom on Monday. He says he has a job for me, a permanent job. Something we can build a future on. So you keep that smile on your face and let's go and take a look at this flat."

She leans over the table and kisses him. "I love you," she tells him, and I can see she really does.

"I know," he replies.

As they get up to leave, I can see an extra light inside of her. She is pregnant. As they walk out the door of the café, I find myself standing in a kitchen. It is the same woman, now heavily pregnant. She is standing over a cooker, getting dinner ready. The front door opens and the man from the café comes in.

"Hello love." She greets him with a kiss, her energy lights up.

"Dinner smells nice," he tells her.

"Did you get paid?" she asks.

"No, but don't start. I will, I promise. I am meeting Malcom in the pub, and he has it waiting for me," he tells her.

"Are you sure? The landlord came knocking today, he wants the rent and next week's too," she tells him.

"I'm just going to run upstairs and change into a clean shirt for a quick pint with Malcom, then I'll be back. Tomorrow I will go see misery-guts myself and pay him."

He winks and then goes upstairs. I can see him. He is putting some clothes into a holdall. He reaches into the cupboard and pulls out a rolled up sock, sticks his hand inside and pulls out a lot of money. He stuffs some more clothes into the holdall, walks to the bedroom door and looks down the stairs. Stepping back, he opens a window and drops the holdall onto the ground outside. He walks downstairs into the kitchen.

"I won't be long," he tells her.

"Don't be, please," she pleads.

He smiles at her, cups her head in his hand and kisses her. "Our luck is changing. It's gonna be OK."

He walks out of the house, picks up his holdall and walks down the road.

Elaine smiles at me and walks out of the house. I follow and as I go through the door I'm on a new street. It's daytime. The street is lined with nice detached houses, each front garden has a well-tended hedge, pristine lawn and a few have cars in the driveways. Some cherry blossom blows across in front of me and I watch it float on the wind. As I follow it I see a large building in the background and myself falling off. My stomach knots and I am unsteady on my feet. I turn round to look for Elaine. She is standing in a driveway and coming towards her is the pregnant lady, but now she is holding a baby in her arms. She walks up to the house with the cherry tree in blossom and turns onto the drive. She knocks on the front door. A lady in her fifties opens the door.

"Hello love!"

"Hi Mum."

"How have you been?" the lady asks.

"Can I come in, Mum?"

"Sorry, of course you can!" She steps aside and then leans out of the door and looks up and down the street.

"Would you like to hold your granddaughter, Mum?" she says, presenting the child to her.

"I will just let your father know you're here. Why don't you go and sit in there?" she says, pointing to a door.

She goes into the room and sits down. Her mum returns with her dad.

"Would you like to hold your granddaughter, Dad?" she asks.

"No," he replies.

"I have named her Elaine, after you, Mum," she tells them.

"You shouldn't have," her dad replies.

"I know you're angry, but..."

He interrupts: "Angry? I'm not angry! Ashamed, oh yes I'm ashamed. You're not my daughter and that, that... YOU SLUT!" he shouts. "How dare you bring that into my house?"

He storms out of the room.

"Your father needs time," Elaine's mum is told.

"Mum, I need help. I have nowhere to live, no food..."

Her mother gets up and walks over to a side cabinet. She pulls a tin out from a drawer. Inside is some money. She takes it all and hands it over to her daughter. She walks to the front door and opens it.

"You should leave."

Elaine's mum stands up and takes Elaine with her.

"Mum..." she says.

Her mum looks down at the floor and shakes her head. Her daughter steps out onto the drive and her mum looks up.

"It's probably best you don't come back, dear. Your father hasn't been his best lately. He's doing a lot of hours at work, important projects..." she trails off.

"Not the greatest start to your life then?" I say to Elaine.

"It's the start I agreed to," she replies.

We walk down the street, merge into a new road. It's late at night, we are standing outside a terraced house. I can see through the window, a man sitting in a chair, drinking. He finishes the drink and picks up a bottle, which is empty also. He tosses it across the room. He walks over to a handbag and rummages through it, pulling out a purse. He finds nothing and throws that across the room too. He goes upstairs into a bedroom where Elaine's mum is sleeping. He grabs her by the hair and lifts her across the room and drags her downstairs. She holds on tight to his hands, trying to stop him pulling the hair clean out of her scalp. She is dragged into the sitting room and dropped on the floor. He picks up the purse and throws it at her.

"Where is the money?" he screams at her.

"We've spent it," she replies.

"You mean you've spent it, you and that kid."

"We needed food," she tells him.

He walks out of the room into the kitchen and pulls a hammer from the drawer. He takes the hammer and starts to smash away at the money box on the electric meter. Elaine's mum gets up, runs into the kitchen and tries to grab the hammer.

"Don't! Leave the money. They'll send you to prison this time."

He pushes her off and swings the hammer onto the coin box. Fifty-pence pieces spill out onto the floor. She tries to grab some of the money, he pushes her back and she falls back cracking her head on the cooker as she goes down. While he is picking up the money, dazed she crawls across the floor to the doorway. She pulls herself up, and the back of her night dress is bloodstained.

"Please..." she pleads, holding up her arms, trying to stop him leaving. He pushes her to one side and walks through the door. She grabs hold of his arm.

"We need that money," she screams, pulling harder, trying to hold him back. He turns round and punches her in the jaw. Elaine's mum drops to the ground. He picks up his jacket and walks out. I look at Elaine: she is unphased by it all.

In the morning, daylight pours through the window, the front door is wide open. A small child dressed in pink pyjamas with yellow daffodils on stands in the doorway – it's Elaine. She has come downstairs and walked into the room to see her mum lying on the floor.

"Mummy?" the child calls out.

The young Elaine calls out a few times. She walks out of the house and knocks on next door's door. A Mrs Abingale answers the door.

"Mummy won't wake up," she tells Mrs Abingale.

"Frank," Mrs Abigale calls her husband. He comes to the door. "Elaine says she can't wake her mum up."

Frank goes off to check. He walks into the house and finds Elaine's mum on the floor. Seeing the broken furniture, the hammer and blood, Frank rings an ambulance and the police. They all arrive very quickly, and Elaine's mum comes round with the help of the paramedics. Elaine is able to sit on her mum's lap and tells her very proudly how she went next door to fetch help for her mummy. Despite the preceding events, the two of them do seem very happy. Elaine's mum has an energy of love about her: she adores her daughter.

"Right then, let's get you off to the hospital," the ambulance driver tells Elaine's mum. He turns to the young Elaine. "Why don't you come with us and ride in the back of the ambulance with your mum?" The young Elaine nods excitedly.

On her return from hospital, Elaine and her mother notice the front door slightly ajar. They walk in and are met by one of the policemen from earlier in the day.

"Everything alright?" Elaine's mum asks the policeman.

"No, not really," a female voice says, from the kitchen. A woman walks into the room.

"I am Mrs Fetch, from social services. I have been alerted about your drinking and accidents, falling over and other such things..."

"Well, hang on a second, Mrs Fetch," The policeman says. "We do believe Albert Rankle is responsible for this, and the marks on the poor lady's face."

"Nevertheless, officer, it is my unfortunate job to investigate, and until I am satisfied the young girl is safe and this poor lady is not responsible, I shall be taking the young girl into care."

"No!" Elaine's mum protests.

"Are you sure that is really necessary?" the police officer asks.

"Yes! Quite necessary. There is enough evidence here for concern and clearly this Albert Rankle is an unhinged man. It will be safer if the young girl comes with me until you apprehend the vulgar beast, and I can carry out the appropriate checks on the mother," Mrs Fetch says.

And with that, Mrs Fetch picks up an already packed suitcase and takes the young Elaine.

"I never saw Mum again, I spent my years in children's homes and at eighteen I was thrown out onto the street to fend for myself. I met a lady, Mrs Haggerty; she took in young girls and introduced us to men with needs, as she would call them. For a few quid a week she gave you a room and men with needs knew where to find us," Elaine tells me.

"So what now?" I ask.

We step outside onto the street. It is raining, and at the end of the road is Elaine's mum. She is wearing a summer dress and clutching a doll to her chest. The rain pours down and the hours pass and she stands there looking down the street. Passers-by ignore her at first and then some start to gather and talk about what they should do. Some who know her mention she hasn't been right since her child was taken last year, and mutterings of terrible business can be heard. Elaine walks up to her mum and circles her, looking at her mum, shivering and holding the drenched doll as tightly as she can. A shop owner eventually comes over and ushers her mum into a shop and scolds a few of the passers-by, letting them know it is time to move on and attend to their own lives.

"He called mum a doctor and mum was sectioned. I grew up feeling abandoned and unloved. My mum loved me so much that when they took me, and she learnt she would never see me again, she broke down and never recovered. I was so angry, I never once checked to find out what happened. And that was the choice I made, the choice I carried through life. The choice I could have taken was to find my mum, heal our wounds," Elaine tells me.

"And now?" I ask.

"There." Elaine points to the other side of the garden we are now standing in. On a bench is an old lady holding a doll to her chest. As Elaine walks over, her aura changes to a golden shimmer, and a golden light connects to her mum. She looks up and sees Elaine.

Elaine kneels down in front of her mum, their fore-
heads touch, and her hand reaches up to Elaine's face.
Elaine takes her other hand and the doll in her hands.
The golden light expands around them. I sense that
very soon mum and daughter will be reunited.

10TH FLOOR

"Think about perception," the tramp says to me.

I try to become aware of perception.

"Ask yourself why you are here," the tramp says, listening to my thoughts.

"It's Limbo Park," I reply.

I have eternity. This thought comes into my head, quickly followed by another. I have as many times as I need and I can go as many times as needed.

"Good," says the tramp. "Now, what is eternity? And how many times and how many places?"

"Eternity is everlasting. There is no time frame, I can take as long as I require or choose any life path. I can try again and again. It is unlimited and it can be any place I choose. Limbo Park is not real; it is a place manifested by my perception of what should happen when I die as it is for the others here." I reply out loud, although I am not sure if I am speaking or having my thoughts read.

"Why are you here?" the tramp asks again.

I think about this, but the answers are not ready or do not come to me. I think to myself that I am here because of my perception, and as I haven't hit the ground my soul has taken a leave of absence from my body. The tramp found me and put me here and I believed her. She created a perception I wouldn't challenge. Limbo Park is here because I believe what I am presented.

"How are you able to do this?" I ask.

"I am a fully realised soul," she replies.

A realised soul, a fully realised soul, is released from physical limitations. I am missing a part of me, or part of me is missing. I am only part of who I really am, a section of an experience for the soul. I have separated to enjoy human life and return with the experience. When I returned I would have reunited with the soul and become whole again, a fully realised soul. But I cannot reunite, not yet. The journey is not complete. I have not severed myself from the body or the physical influence of Earth perception.

"I presented this perception to you, a pleasant park, familiar like the many parks you have seen, and you accept it and enjoy it. As this present moment moves and you learn more, you can start to change your perceptions," the tramp tells me.

"Do you collect souls?" I ask the tramp.

"No," she says smiling. "At least not in the way you think. Someone would have gathered you up, but you crossed my path instead."

"So it was an accident," I reply.

"I've never experienced an accident," she says. "Come on, it's time to see more."

I get up and follow the tramp. I think about the tramp's bench. It looks like a fallen tree shaped into a bench, but it's alive. It is a fully mature Sweet Chestnut in full blossom, growing on its side, the middle of the trunk shaped like a bench. We are walking through the tramp's flower meadow towards a lake. There are butterflies fluttering between the many flowers, beautiful and vibrant in colour, each one with its own distinct shade and vibration. The vibration helps make the colour of the thousands of flowers, maybe even millions, of the tramp's meadow perception. They are all individual, just like on Earth; we think they are the same, they look alike, but if you were able to examine them through the soul's eyes you would see the differences. The tramp has created this perception with awareness of every flower, grass stem and butterfly.

"How do you..." the tramp interrupts me.

"I understand the whole, realise they are all individual, and then accept that they are all very different. I also know that they exist and do not exist at the same time. When I stop looking, they have gone, and when I sit on my bench it is all in front of me again."

I stop walking. "How the hell does something exist and not exist at the same time?" I ask.

"You see it and I see it, so it exists, but I accept it is not real, so I am not attached to it. In this way it doesn't exist. Do you really think I am a tramp sitting on a bench in a park? Your perception of what you see does not make it the truth."

We walk past the lake and head towards an embankment. As we go over the top of the embankment, I see the town I lived in and the building I have stepped off. As I look closer, I can see myself falling, and I also see myself standing on top of the building before I stepped off. We walk through the air, across the rooftops, everything as I remembered before I was falling. I am feeling hesitant as I come closer to my falling physical body, an uncertainty, perhaps fear that I will be placed back inside my physical body to continue until I have hit the floor, just to experience the trauma. A memory for the soul to bring into the next life as a prevention mechanism, so I will not do it again. As I get closer, I notice just how incompatible the human body is with flying, yet how perfect it is for falling. This is a strange thought; I think to myself. My apprehension has receded. I feel no remorse or attachment. I was expecting to be jolted by some feeling or realisation, an event to make me understand the magnitude of my actions, but nothing. Although the body is falling, to me time really has no place, just a constant presence and experience of "now". I am not hindered by the past or the future. I see into my eyes, and they have a dullness to them, missing the sparkle of life I once saw in my reflection. When I used to stare into the mirror, deep into my own eyes, my soul could see itself looking back. Now, as I look deep into my eyes, I see my old companion, the ego. Since our brief separation, I know just how separate we really are. He is sitting in the corner of my subconscious, his knees pulled up to his chest, arms wrapped around his legs, rocking back and forth. He notices me, staring in.

"Changed your mind, have you?" he asks.

I smile.

"Thought not," he says, and then gets up and walks towards the front of my subconscious. He is wearing a red jumper and dark blue jeans; how different we are. I would never have worn that in our lifetime.

"You and I, we could have done so much more," he says, his hand flicking back, pointing at me and then himself, his voice breaking.

"Souls. You bloody know it all, don't you, but you won't share! Life is not important, is it? Not to you, it's all perception, none of it real. I have to struggle on, knowing you know how to change my life, how to create the perception," he pauses, tears in his eyes overflowing onto his cheeks. He sits back in the corner. His voice softens. "You don't really understand us. You decide a package before you come, what to do, how to experience. Then, to create choice and freewill so that you can "learn", you throw in an ego, and it's always my fault. I can't have eternity. There is no nirvana for me. I am born knowing I will die, and you want me to share your bliss. I live day-to-day in fear I could be struck down by illness, hit by a car... or better still, your cruellest trick, we live to be old, in an ever-deteriorating body, with all the humiliation of growing old and needing care. And I am supposed to be grateful because each day I am alive is your choice, a day you have traded for an experience, for "learning", every day a school day to you... It's not for me. Every day is a day of fear."

Memories filter back to me, my first ego many centuries ago, and there have been thousands of egos, maybe more. Egos and souls were close, at the beginning. Souls were not as quiet as we are now. The secrets we know were shared readily, we were naïve souls, pure in light and love, wrapped up in the bliss of happiness. The ego introduced us to lust, and we absorbed it like a drug. Then, like all addicts, we could not get enough to satisfy our craving for decadence and power. The first time souls entered physical bodies, they were inexperienced, to gain experience is an integral part of growth for a soul. The first souls incarnated and returned with great stories, with later incarnations souls explored the depths of their feelings. It was exciting, combined with the egos, every incarnation was a new beginning, a new teaching. Until fear was explored, jealously towards another. The souls began a new experience, different from love. This was a powerful emotion, it empowered the ego and with it a lust for control over another. It wasn't long before some souls and egos became gods, changing what they wanted, and clashing with other likeminded egos. With the knowledge of the souls in physical perception, we waged war. Those that dared, killed! And once this happened, egos became frightened. It wasn't long before we were feared and demanded worship. And as new souls were born into the world, they were raised in this environment to worship or be dammed. They lost their perception and their ability to create. Eventually, a few new souls used this knowledge against the so called gods, and through their own fear that it would happen to them, they put a stop to the teachings. The knowledge we are all born with was denied, without nurturing the new souls it was forgotten, and the egos took control. With this truth came limitations: the truth was supposed to set us free, to liberate us, but we were young souls who had never been on a physical plane before. It took many lifetimes to understand the dangers of the physical plane, to realise the soul and ego are designed to co-exist, and it takes many more lifetimes to become realised enough to do this. When we left our bodies, our reign on this physical plane over, we returned, no longer addicted to the lust of physical life and released from the emotions created by the ego. What we saw were the lost experiences, the pain we had caused. As a marker of our grand legacies we got to watch souls do it all over again, creating suffering, demanding worship, reflecting everything we had shown them, only with more imagination. I killed a few; they killed thousands, burnt down villages, wiped out generations. I watched this many times over, knowing my part, and listened to men and women toast my name and offer their victories to me. They stood on bloodstained battlegrounds, shouting my name in honour. When the souls returned, I would be there to meet them, to guide them through the process of returning. They would come back to this plane realising their atrocities, and look to me wanting to know how it had happened and why I didn't intervene. It was more difficult then, now we understand the many times we live this physical life, and the place of the ego. We have always had the ability to control the ego: we choose not to, and then we learnt silence was a good option and eventually through reincarnation the souls will develop to be on the physical plane until then we go on learning. This is our purpose.

"You're being a little hard on yourself," the tramp says. "This is a memory, long before your soul evolved. Ultimately, we all come from the same source, so there are shared memories, just like animals, born with instinct of what to do without any input from their parents."

"It's not me then? I didn't do all of that?" I ask.

"As the greater conscious of all the souls grows with experience, the conscious expands, and with this expansion, souls continue to divide. Like a family tree we are all traceable back to a single soul line. This connection is similar to a DNA strand, a pool of genetic memories within your energy frequency, those souls have evolved almost back to the start of their beginning, and in truth, it could not have happened without the supposed atrocities. Growth isn't just about condemning those who do things you don't like; without this how would you know what you want? Growth comes from searching through all of the experiences and realising you control how it affects you, and what part you choose to play. The event is irrelevant, how it affected you is your choice, and always will be." the tramp tells me.

9TH FLOOR

return to Limbo Park, Darren is sitting on the bench and I walk over to him.

"How's it going?" I ask.

"Good. Very good. I've seen my family switching off the life support machine. They are preparing me to go back," Darren says.

"What happened?"

"I was watching my wife in the hospital ward and I tried to talk to her again. I didn't think she could hear me. She was sitting by my bedside and I was pleading with her to switch off the machine. Then the pastor walked in. As I was about to ask her for help, she smiled and I just knew why she was there. She touched my wife on the chest and I saw this spark of light, this energy ball started to grow outwards, and my wife broke down and cried. Then she told me to talk to my wife." Darren continued, "I was about to speak when my wife spoke.

'Baby, I miss you so much. I have been trying to tell you for so long how much I love you and I am scared. I was unfaithful. I never intended it to happen, and I don't love him. You and I, we stopped talking. I was lonely. You were working so hard, I missed the times we laughed together. I know you did it to provide the best for me, but in the end you weren't there and I hated you for trying so hard. I remember the last time we went to the park: we made up a picnic basket, a bottle of wine, and went down by the lake. It was night time, the sky was so clear, we looked up at the stars and told them our dreams. When we stopped talking we held each other and I leaned back, you put your arms around me and I never wanted anything else. That was four years ago, and then you got that job and you were gone. I was happy at first: no bills to worry about, the house looked nice... But it was empty, and so am I'," Darren tells me, "My wife broke down in tears. I ain't never heard her sob like that before. I didn't know what to say; the energy ball disappeared and I started to feel sad as well. She was right: I worked long hours and always blamed it on doing my best for her. I wanted her to have everything."

The tramp appears and signals to Darren to follow her, I look over and she signals me also. As the three of us walk across the well-kept lawns of Darren's park, the scenery changes. We're walking on a stone floor inside a narrow passage. There are candles on the wall, lighting our way, the ceiling is arched and made of carved stone. We enter a large hall filled with people

going about their business. Everyone is dressed so differently, as if we're at a huge fancy dress party. People
from every era of history can be seen walking across
the hall. I look up and I can see people walking across
the air. I manage to make out outlines of transparent
paths, another floor, no, another dimension. Realising
I have become distracted, I chase after Darren and the
tramp. As I catch up to them, we are being led to a door
which appears only when you are within its vicinity.
We go inside the room. There is an old man sitting at
a desk on the left. The room is filled, floor to ceiling,
with shelves of scrolls, bulging out, some look old,
and others look new. The old man looks up from his
desk and nods to the tramp, she looks at Darren and
the shelves start to move. Shelf after shelf passes us by,
they start to slow down and then stop. A scroll lights
up and falls on to the old man's desk. He opens the
scroll, Darren and I peer over his shoulder; the scroll
is blank. We look at each other, confused, and watch as
the old man continues to read and then mutter to himself. After a few minutes, the old man looks around,
smiles, and nods to the tramp.

"Sit over there please, Darren," the old man says, and
pulls out a chair. Darren sits down and is handed the
open scroll. Darren takes the scroll and holds it up to
show me: it's still blank. We both shrug our shoulders.
I turn to look at the tramp, but she has gone, as has the
old man. I head towards the door and they both appear

again. I turn back to look at Darren and he is a glowing light. He has companions of light by his side and they are all looking at the scroll. Beams of energy orbit Darren and his companions. Some of the energy is pulled from the air and placed on the scroll, lighting up as if it is being written down. I want to speak to Darren, so I step into the beams of energy. Symbols and words are swirling around me, but I cannot see Darren or his companions. I reach up to try and take one of the energies: they pass through me, changing colour from gold to pink, yellow to blue, swirling around to form clouds of colour, changing and then separating, then joining with other streams of energies coming in from the ether. I feel information being pulled from me as if I am downloading, and then I realise. Darren may have been having his scroll written for his return, but I am being readied also. With this realisation my form changes. I lose my familiar human structure. I see the tramp, the bright light with a violet edge. The old man is a yellow light. My surroundings no longer have walls and all of the people I saw are now forms of light, different sizes, shapes and colours. As I look outwards I see an endless pink, just like a soft sunset, and as the different energies move around they affect their immediate area just like the colour spectrum. Red and yellow make orange, red and blue make purple, blue and yellow make green, all different energies lighting up, moving and mixing into a kaleidoscope of colours, continually changing as people move around.

They are getting me ready to return. I gain a sense of a greater whole, the only limitations is my perception and my own evolution. The steps I have taken to become more aware, the many lessons over many journeys, the experience on the earth plane and the ones in spirit: the lessons only continue as we grow, and with each evolution we move to another level, another existence. I am still an earthly energy, bound by my actions, my body still falling. I have to see life through to its natural end and I find myself realising, at its most basic premise, one of the fundamental points of life. Choice! And what choices did I make to promote my life? So I will return and start again.

8TH FLOOR

Back at Limbo Park, I think about what has just happened. Why Darren? And what do the scrolls mean? I see the tramp walking along the side of the lake and walk over to her. She doesn't look at me but, as always, knows I am there. I am about to ask a question.

"Shhh!" the tramp says.

And I am standing in a library.

"Think the question and look for the book," she instructs me.

What are the scrolls? I ask myself. I stand and wait, a minute passes, and I feel the need to walk around the shelves, aimlessly at first. But then I know which shelf and head towards the book I want. The book is leather bound, A4 in size, not very thick with little weight, and has no title on the cover. None of the books have titles. I take another book and try to open it, but it is stuck closed. I open my book to the first page and it reads All You Need to Know. I turn to the next page, the contents.

Chapter One: How to Use this Book
Chapter Two: Your Questions Answered

I turn to the next page.

How to Use this Book.

In trying to use this book the reader must first under-stand that this book is for them alone and does not apply to anyone else. You must also know we cannot answer a question you are not able to conceive the possibility of understanding. An example of this, a child asks a parent why it rains. The child will not understand the meteoro-logical science of the atmosphere and weather patterns so a parent will adjust their answer to the child's level of understanding and hopefully the child will gain more knowledge in the process enabling them to develop.

I turn to the next page.

To use this book, first close the book think of your question, and the reopen at Chapter Two.

I close the book and think again of my question: What are the scrolls? I open the book at Chapter Two.

The first part of the scroll records the lifetimes you have had. The second part of the scroll records what you have done in those lifetimes. The third records what is left to do.

The scrolls are an agreement your soul has made with itself. Written on the scroll is the type of life you wish to have, the people you may meet, the influences you may have and how your life may end up. It is written as a record of what you wanted to achieve, when you wanted to achieve this and how it may happen. All the scrolls allow for circumstances to change. If you stray too far away from the path you had intended, circumstances may change to bring you back. The rules are based on the lesson you asked to experience and learn from.

I close the book, thinking to myself that I must have agreed for my life to take this direction. Did I agree to suicide at the beginning? I think to ask the book and open Chapter Two.

NO.

I shut the book and think: Why did this happen? I open Chapter Two.

You chose this to happen, it is your free will.

I close the book and think this is complicated. We have free will, choices and yet we live a predetermined life. Explain!

I open the book.

No life is predetermined as you have perceived it. You decided before descending the journey you wish to take; however, your own free will allows for changes in direction. When you stand on a bridge and drop a stick into the water, the stick will flow down the river until the journey has ended. No matter how many sticks you drop into the water even though it is flowing in the same direction they will all travel their own journey. When in life you reach a fork in the river, you decide which fork you will take. Sometimes it is not the guided decision, and this will lead you along a different journey in the same river. You can always take the unguided forks, but you will still arrive at the end of the river with the other sticks. Some will get there before you and some will arrive later. All of the sticks will have their own scars and all of the sticks will have absorbed the water along the way. You were not guided to jump! But you chose that river journey anyway and the journey still continues for you and will continue until you complete the evolution. You descend and then ascend to return.

I close the book. How do we know or learn the right way, the guided way to go?

The decision that brings you joy will always be the right one. Listen for the joy: if a choice makes you smile or presents an opportunity then this is the right choice. Sometimes you are guided and you use your gut instinct. Sometimes you pray and ask for something to come into your life. This is often presented with a lesson to learn; an experience that will make you understand what you have gained. Mrs Right often only arrives because you met Mrs Wrong, you cannot fully appreciate the experience without the other.

"It's time to move on," the tramp tells me.

"Not yet, I have more questions!" I reply.

"Such as?" the tramp enquires.

"I sense this is not the way for everyone, so why is my heaven different?"

"Every soul has a different need. When you leave the physical world you will have learnt preconceived ideas of what Heaven, the afterlife is. When you die of old age, or expect this to happen, the soul makes preparations to return and it is not surprised or unfamiliar to the journey. Sometimes when the cause is sudden and unexpected you will have a period of limbo, a time of adjustment, and people you once knew will appear and help you. This will only last until you shake off the weight of the physical world. When, as with you, the line of the soul has not been severed, you are unable to fully expand or return to your real energy. You are still connected to the physical plane, so this heaven is partly your creation of what should happen when you die, and partly my assistance in making somewhere appear to be a heaven. I have filled in the blanks and moved you along, making you ready for your return. Your soul is still connected to the body falling from the building, so you cannot begin to experience the fullness of the afterlife," the tramp explains.

7TH FLOOR

Having been told I cannot experience the fullness of the afterlife, I feel unconnected. I am consciously aware of the restraints of the physical body and my limitations. I sit on my bench, looking at my body falling through the air, and for the first time I see the silver line connecting me to my body, as thin as a spider's thread, but very strong. I am being held, not against my will, but against my soul. My celebration at the beginning, when I thought I had freed myself from the life, believing I was in my afterlife, the joy of experiencing new, greater energies, more understanding, feelings of love and joy I had never felt as a person... This no longer releases me. I now feel the burden of time and physicality. I know I am far away from something greater, a joyous freedom where it is not possible to feel suffocated by life, an existence that has never remembered anxiety or fear. At the next level we cannot carry impurity, burden is not only an unknown word, it is not possible because we are truly free. The original source of who I am has not abandoned me: I am unable to return until my journey down the river has finished. This moment of existence right now is a break, if you like. I have reached the river bank and for a fleeting time I have climbed onto the grassy verge and rested in the summer sun.

I sense it's time for me to see Darren. I find him in his hospital room, this time not outside his body, but inside. He doesn't notice me. He has returned completely, his family are there saying their goodbyes, telling Darren that they love him. One by one they leave the room. His wife, holding his tear soaked hand in hers, nods to the nurse, and she switches off his life support machine. After a few moments a glow starts to emit from Darren's body, and slowly a light ebbs out, gathering about eight inches overhead. This bright light takes on an orange glow with a violet edge and forms into a butterfly; I guess that's how I want to see it. His wings flutter and he flies upwards and joins thousands of butterflies in a stream of light heading towards the afterlife.

"I feel your sadness," says the tramp appearing at my side.

"I am feeling sad, seeing Darren leave. I am realising this is as far as I go," I reply.

"You shouldn't worry, your higher self has changed things for you," she tells me.

"This doesn't make me feel better," I reply.

"Let's go and look at the life Darren is going to enjoy," the tramp suggests.

Within a footstep I am walking on sand, the sea is still and sunbathers are enjoying a hot summer. The beach is busy: a mixture of tourists and locals, every hundred yards or so there is a beach hut selling drinks and snacks, playing music, families dining together and young couples discovering first love.

"Where are we?" I ask.

"Barcelona," I am told.

"Darren wasn't from Barcelona," I point out.

"No one is from Earth," the tramp replies, smiling.

We walk along the beach until we reach the harbour, where the local fishermen are bringing in their catch. Children are sitting on the harbour walls fishing and there is a bustle of excitement as a boy pulls out a fish. He holds it up and shouts out to a fisherman coming in, he nods and instructs him to bring it to his boat. The boy runs round, trying not to drop his slippery catch. He greets the fisherman with his arms held out, showing him the prize. The fisherman examines the fish and pulls some money out of his pocket, and a deal is done. The boy runs back to his friends shouting and waving the money in the air, and one by one they cast out fresh lines, hoping they will catch the next one.

"This is a nice place. When does Darren arrive?" I ask.

"He is here." The tramp points back along the beach. "Over there."

"I don't see him," I tell her.

The tramp points to a couple sitting on the sand. The woman is pregnant.

"His parents," the tramp tells me. "Amile and Ricardo. They are now the proud owners of that building." The tramp points to a rundown two-storey building, the windows have been boarded up and the bottom floor is covered in graffiti.

"It doesn't look much," I reply, unimpressed.

"It might not look much to you, but Ricardo and Amile have saved up, taken out a mortgage to make that their business and home. It will be an independent coffee shop, selling light snacks, some seats outside to enjoy breakfast, lunch or an evening coffee right on the beach. They have talked about these dreams with real passion and the universe will deliver. Darren will grow up here, and if he is guided well and listens to his heart, he will enjoy his life by the sea and never want to leave. He will take over the family business, buy the shop next door and have a family with the girl he will meet seventeen years from now. He is going to serve her a coffee and his heart will skip a beat when he looks into her eyes. She will return over the next week or so, and he will ask her out, and when he does her heart will skip a beat too."

I look at Amile and Ricardo; they are very much in love and Barcelona is a beautiful place. As I look at them both, I can see the excitement as an energy sur-rounding them. It is growing and strong. This will be a wonderful place to grow up with the potential for a great life.

The tramp has gone and I am watching the passers-by. It seems like forever since I was back on Earth, and somewhere as I watch this world my body is falling. Again, I think to myself that I am not ready to go back. I wonder if there is an escape, and I shudder and feel my energy distort. If I could breathe, it would have taken my breath away. I take that as a sign to accept my fate. I decide to sit on the beach. It is night time now, and I can see the ships as they sail by. The port in Barcelona is busy and there are many ships on the horizon. The moon is bright tonight and the water still. Amile and Ricardo are sitting at one of the beach huts. Ricardo is scribbling on his notepad, making plans for their future. He and Amile discuss this, and I can see the energy pouring out to the universe so strongly it creates pictures in my mind. I take the thoughts and think about Darren's future. It is hazy at first, I guess because I am trying to see ahead of myself, and as each moment passes I can feel myself being pulled back. Darren is about fourteen. It is a sunny day. Ricardo and Amile have their coffee shop and it looks nice; they have table and chairs outside under a canopy, the once boarded-up front is now glass, which folds open giving the feeling of sitting on the beach when inside. At the counter are homemade ice-creams, pastries, sandwiches and an array of drinks. Darren is outside, waiting on tables. Some of his friends come by, asking him to come and play football. Darren tells them he is working, "Making money for the family," he says laughing. Ricardo comes out of the coffee shop and tells Darren to go and play football with his friends, adding if it gets busy he will call him back. Darren agrees and follows his friends. Amile calls Darren back and hands him some cold drinks to share with his friends. This is definitely a life Darren will enjoy: he has chosen well.

6TH FLOOR

"Come on. You can't sit and watch other people's lives. You have your own to get on with," the tramp says. "You're going to meet your guides."

We walk along a beach at night. We have moved on from Barcelona, the stars are bright and the moon full. I can see someone waiting for us, and sure enough the tramp stops and nods in the direction of the stranger. As I get closer, I can see a samurai warrior. He puts his hand to his katana and unsheathes it slightly, I pause and he nods resting the katana back in its sheath.

"I am Yatoyya," he says.

"Yato-to-to-yaya," I stutter.

"Ya-toy-ya," he replies sternly. "I am here to teach you, and in your next life I will guide you. If you listen, this bond will become strong."

"What, like a medium?" I say excitedly.

"No," Yatoyya replies, sternly once more.

"Before you return we will teach you new lessons, lessons of the soul. This will help you to understand, in your new life, what is important and what is not."

"Don't we know already?" I ask.

"If quizzed and made to think, you would know the right answer, but this is an imprint, a much stronger impression to help guide you," Yatoyya says.

Yatoyya looks across the sand, and instructs me to stand with my feet together and we begin to pace along the beach.

"Now, we walk more casually," he says.

We continue our walk along the beach, sometimes the waves washing over my feet. As the beach curves round, we come to a large rock and sit down. Yatoyya points back to where we have walked.

"The philosophy of many incarnations," he says. "Sitting here, I am unable to notice my footsteps in the sand; the waves have taken some of them long ago. A footstep in the sand, a moonlit night, a sunny day, no matter the where or the time, it is not important. It never has been. As I press each naked foot into the sand, one leaves an impression slightly different to the last one and the next – they seem the same at first, but closer examination, if it were possible, would reveal that I have left different impressions and the sands are different. Washed away by different waves, some impressions last a little longer than others, an example, perhaps, that although practised in the art of walking, we still do it unevenly; or maybe the waves treat each step we take a little differently. The wave that has travelled a thousand miles to land on the beach, maybe, has great momentum and crashes down when it finally arrives. Another wave is a ripple, and with grace rolls up and climbs the beach as if stretching out on a bed, finally glad to be at rest. Footsteps in the sand are the many times we return, each step a lifetime, an impression made before being swept away, now no longer noticed, at best a memory of joy and laughter for loved ones. If time would permit an examination, we'd notice the nuances that made each step different to the last, a reminder that no matter how practised we are at living, we will always come back and do it differently. The sands of time do not stop for anyone, and nor do the waves that wash them away. When the final journey of all journeys comes to its last stop, will I be able to stand at the end of my own private beach and look back to see a thousand footsteps, some graceful, some unsteady? At the end, will my last impression be deep and unmoved by waves, a permanent mark of who I have been? Or will I grace the sand so gently I will have left no impression at all. The point at the end is to know it does not matter. All impressions will be washed away, the grains of sand we once touched will have a memory of an impression we made, but these grains of sand will be rolled by many waves and the impressions we made will not have a lasting impact. A lifetime to us is just a grain of sand rolling on the beach; sometimes the waves have an impact on our impressions of life."

As I sit and ponder what I have just been told, Yatoyya holds out his hand. A marble-sized orb of light appears, and floats upwards from his hand, stopping in front of my face. I can see symbols and energies, just as when I saw the scrolls.

"Take it," Yatoyya says.

I hold out my hand and the orb sinks into my palm. As I look at my hands I can see a faint glow of light, and I feel the meaning of the story within me.

5TH FLOOR

"Come, it is time to meet another guide," Yatoyya says.

A few steps along the beach I find myself walking through long grass. It is night, and as always the moonlight allows me to see the way. We enter a wood, and through the trees I see an orange glow. As I approach a clearing, sitting by a fire I see the tramp and a Native American. Yatoyya looks at them they nod and start to chuckle. Yatoyya sits down by the fire, the Native American gestures me to sit also.

"Show me what you have learnt," he says.

"Well, erm, our lives are..." he interrupts me. "Show me. Hold out your hand and show me."

I hold out my hand and the orb appears, floating over my palm. The Native American stands up and looks into the orb. I see the symbols again, and a connection forms between the orb and the Native American, information transfers between the two of them then the orb drops back into my hand.

"This is good. It will be of great use to you when you return. Please, sit," he says, gesturing me to take a seat.

As I oblige, the Native American rummages through a bag and pulls out a beech tree nut.

"Take it," he says offering it to me.

"Now, hold it in your hand, and look at the nut. This nut is the seed of the mighty beech tree. It contains all of the knowledge it needs to grow and mature, and the seed knows the circle of life before it has begun."

I look at the nut and focus my attention, looking at its surface. The outside of the nut is a hard shell with spikes, at the top is an opening revealing a shiny brown kernel. The flames flicker in the background and I see a light inside the seed, then a symbol just as it was with the Native American and the orb. The seed tells me a story.

The Circle of Life.

I remember sitting under the cover of the leaves, they were just starting to turn colour for a golden autumn. I didn't know about autumn then; I was just a beech nut, still attached to the tree. One day a wind picked up and came through the woods, stronger than winds I had felt before and cold, carrying whispering voices from faraway lands. This wind started pushing the branches against themselves, leaves were falling, and all of the wood came alive. As the wind pushed a branch one way, the tree would whip it back another. I was scared; it was the first time I had witnessed such a violent event. Old branches snapped off, loud cracks could be heard as big branches fell to the ground, some crashing on top of smaller trees below.

Then it happened. I could feel the wind pushing, groaning, as it used all of its might to push my branch back further than before.

"Whoa!" I screamed, as the wind let up and my branch slapped back, launching me into the air. I landed next to an old fallen tree. I managed to roll underneath, searching for some protection, a shelter from the storm.

"Don't worry, young'un," I heard the tree say, "It's your turn now."

The wind left the woods and came back again several times, then rain and snow. Then one day the sun rose as it had many times, but this time there was warmth with the sunlight. The sun triggered a reaction which changed how I felt, and I tried to expand myself. It was difficult at first, but as I tried harder, I broke out of my shell. I pushed further out, sending tiny roots into the ground. For days I would be exhausted, but I kept on pushing, trying harder and harder with each new day. Soon I had laid my roots, so I dug deeper into the soil. I didn't know why, I was driven by instinct and as the days became longer, the trees around me started growing too, their leaves covering the sky. I stopped pushing my roots downwards and panicked, this time pushing upwards, trying to touch the sun. At night

I would scream at the sun to stay: I wasn't finished! Then I would sleep until the first chattering birds woke me in the morning. I would be waiting, and at the first glimpse of the sun, I would start pushing upwards with everything I had to give. I pushed out two leaves; they helped hold me steady in the afternoon breeze as I grew taller.

That was my first year. A few years later I remember looking at the trees around me. They were massive, their branches reached out further than I was able to see. I am close to the ground: it is a different life for me. The leaves on the ground are a home to many, and I can just see over the old tree I landed next to. It has fungus living on its side, like little steps, only they don't lead anywhere. Beetles come and lay their eggs in the old tree. A badger sometimes visits at night and pulls off the decayed wood, and always seems very happy with whatever it is she finds. The worms in the ground wriggle around my roots, tickling me as they go by. I have noticed that very little grows under the big trees. I am lucky next to my fallen tree. My roots are more settled, and I do not hurry to touch the sun as much as I used to. I like playing with the butter-flies that sunbathe on my leaves. I have eleven leaves and I am getting taller each year. I watch the birds flying from tree to tree, making homes and raising their young. The large tree across from me has three different nests! I came from that tree, and I think

I am the only seed to fall from her and take root. She doesn't talk much, unlike the nettles that grow next to me always chattering away. They told me last year that the large tree was upset as one of her blackbirds had died. She has had the same family of blackbirds nesting for three-hundred years, and she still gets a little upset when one dies. The nettles also told me that the trees never die and we go on for ever and ever.

One-hundred years ago this year, I was thrown from a branch during a windy autumn day and found my footing the next spring. The old fallen tree I used to hide behind has long gone. The nettles are wrong: we do not live on forever as they think. I have raised a few blackbird families myself. I still remember the male blackbird landing on one of my branches. He stood there proudly and started to sing, telling the whole wood I was the tree he would be nesting in. Last year was the last year I saw him. He was too old to carry on through the winter. This saddened me, and it will sadden me more when the first blackbird born on my branches will one day pass. However, I look forward to seeing the hundreds of blackbirds I will give shelter to, catching their young with my branches when they stumble out of the nest a little early. The tree I came from is now the oldest in the woods and starting to wilt. I have asked if I can help, but she just smiles and says she hopes for a chilly, windy autumn, like the one that sent me off behind the fallen tree. I have seen many trees grow old. Some don't fall; come spring you look across and they have not woken up. By the summer you realise they are going back to the earth, but their roots were strong so they have not fallen over yet.

I am three-hundred now, the largest tree in the woods. The tree I came from has gone; the chilly, windy autumn she wanted eventually came and she crashed down, taking another, smaller tree with her. That same night, some beech tree nuts were tossed next to her and, just like me, found shelter under the fallen tree to grow. They also panic just like I did, and it will be some time before they are settled; two of them still panic every spring when the warm sun comes back. I have been lucky to see many different birds raised from my branches, and I still remember the first parents and the great sadness when their first born passed on, so many years ago. Since then I have had many years of joy watching the young ones grow. I am no longer sad when they don't make it; I have seen how life grows over these many years, and I have told the nettles they are wrong; the trees do not live forever as they believe. We return to the ground and hope to give shelter to a beech nut like me. I am nearly the tallest and oldest tree in the woods, yet I still cannot reach the sun. My leaves reach higher than they ever have, yet they are still connected to my mighty roots. They stretch out just as far as my branches and the worms still tickle me as they pass by.

I am not ready for that chilly, windy autumn night. It is many years off for me. I do now understand a little more as I am close to the top of the circle, right next to the new beginnings. The tree I came from was not fighting the wind as I once thought; she needed the wind to throw me next to the fallen tree, knowing it would provide a great opportunity for me to grow. She knew this because she came from the fallen tree. She watched her tree become the biggest and oldest, before crashing to the ground, just as I saw her become the biggest and the oldest before crashing to the ground. We are the same beech trees that have always been here. We grow and seed, then fall to let others grow. This is the honour of being a beech tree. This is how we live forever.

I become aware of my surroundings. The fire is out and it is daylight. The Native American is sitting down, but the tramp and Yatoyya have gone.

"Just like the beech tree, you have come from one source, and no matter how many footsteps you leave in the sand, you are connected to all of them," he tells me.

"I don't know your name," I reply.

"My tribe once called me Nahlin, meaning fleet of foot. And it is with a fleet foot that we must move on."

4ᵀᴴ FLOOR

I follow Nahlin through the woods. An eagle flies overhead, and I see mountains just like those at Limbo Park. As we walk out of the woods I see Limbo Park, this time with rose bushes, carnations, lupins, irises and every other cottage garden flower you could imagine. We walk over to the lake where a lady is sitting. She stands up as we approach. She is young, about eighteen, with long blonde hair.

She holds out her hand to shake mine. "I am Peru. Hello Nahlin," she says.

Nahlin nods and smiles.

"So, now you have met all of your guides," she says.

"Yes. You seem friendlier," I tell her.

"I am!" she says excitedly. "Nahlin is of nature and listens more than he would speak. Yatoyya is of traditions and discipline; his actions are his words. I am more of a human existence, a mothering guide. I'm going to show you the start of your life," Peru tells me.

Peru takes my arm and starts to skip along the bank of the lake. I look back and see the tramp, Yatoyya and Nahlin all smiling at me. The excited energy Peru radiates is infectious, and I soon start to skip along with her. The energy is light, not like the others. Peru reminds me of a time before I had memories. I feel as though I am a baby cradled in my mother's arms. I'm safe, warm and I would be sleepy, but there is another layer to Peru's energy. It's magic, and I am in awe. I skip faster and start to giggle and wave my arms.

We stop outside a cottage. The garden at the front is full of flowers and there is a dirt driveway at the side. We walk up the path and into the house. There is an old woman in the kitchen cooking a stew. The aroma has filled the house.

"This is where you will live," Peru says.

"In this house, with this lady?" I reply.

"Yes," Peru says in a high-pitched voice, rapidly clapping her hands.

"Is she my mother?" I ask.

"Noooooooooo," Peru replies.

A black labrador appears from one of the rooms and jumps up at the front door starting to bark.

"Yes, yes I think our visitor has arrived," the old lady says to her dog. A car has pulled into the drive, and the old lady opens the door to greet her visitor. The dog runs down to the car wagging his tail.

"Hi!" the old lady shouts out, waving her hand, "I have been so excited since you rang me, oh I'm so happy!"

"Are you sure I won't be a bother? It's just until I get back on my feet, I promise," the voice says, a familiar voice.

"Child, I want you to stay until they carry me out in a box, so I hope you never get back on your feet!" the old lady laughs.

The old lady comes back through the front door, followed by Angie.

"I helped her! I got inside her and helped her get away from her boyfriend," I tell Peru.

"Is this my new life?" I ask Peru.

"It's your next one," she replies.

"Betty, that smells wonderful," Angie says, taking a deep breath as she walks into the kitchen.

"And it's ready right now," Bettys replies.

Betty puts on her floral oven gloves and takes some golden topped bread from the oven, placing it on the side. Betty picks up a knife, starts to cut slices, each stroke releasing steam as crumbs fall onto the breadboard. Betty picks up the butter knife and dips it into the butter bowl, scooping up a dollop which melts into the texture of the bread. She lays the bread out on the kitchen table and takes a clay pot from the oven. She lifts off the lid and the room fills with the aroma of lamb casserole. Angie is sitting at the table and has the look of a small girl eagerly anticipating the wonderful meal ahead. In the few minutes Angie has been back in the house I can see that life has returned to her; the energy is flowing through her veins, the house and Betty having an incredible healing effect. Peru and I walk out of the house into the back garden. There is a rambling rose on a wall, a vegetable patch and some apple trees bearing their fruit, at the back are some woods. We walk under the trees and stop. I look back at the house.

"So, this is my next life," I say to Peru.

"Yes it is," Peru replies.

"How do you know I won't make the same mistakes again?" I ask.

"You will make different choices, the end choice might be the same, but your environment will be much more supportive. In your last life your father was not much of a role model. He was an experience you required, and again in this life, that experience has to be learned. Only this time you will have no father."

"Haven't I had that experience?" I ask.

"You haven't completed this life cycle," Peru replies.

"Are you saying I jumped off the building because my dad and I weren't mates?" I ask Peru.

"No. Only you know why you jumped. We've just reset the process. The start of the story will begin as before," Peru tells me.

Some dogs are barking in the woods behind the house and a young boy of about six or seven comes running down a track with his three dogs, black and white border collies. The boy is carrying a fishing rod and a bag with a large trout, he runs past us down the garden and into the kitchen. It is me, I am about nine years old, and looking at the boy I see a reflection of my energy.

"Can we see more of me, more of my future?" I ask.

"No, that isn't what we are doing now. Your higher self is getting ready to receive you and to send you back. This is what you are watching; a part of you you can feel, but haven't found yet," she tells me.

There is a part of me that understands all of this. It knows the truth, has unlimited perception without illusions, the whole of all I am. My soul hasn't come down to earth, only a part of it has: the higher self stays, the part connected to the body by the silver thread. Follow this thread and you will find your whole self, this whole of who you are which stays connected to the energy of the universe. It isn't a greater part of me, it's not a size. It is my highest me, a me which vibrates in tune with the creation of all things.

3RD FLOOR

Standing in the garden I become aware of the preparations that have been made by my higher self. It isn't a conscious awareness; I have a strong feeling I am not complete and there is more to this, an earthy feeling that somewhere behind the scenes someone is busy.

"Remember the story of the beech tree?" Peru asks.

"Yes," I reply.

"There is more to the story, a part of the story for you to know and to hold, to take back with you. It's not just about the beech tree, growth, becoming strong and wise," Peru tells me.

Peru drops a beech seed onto the soil, the seed starts to grow, and soon it is the tallest beech tree I have ever seen. The wind picks up and a storm blows in. The wind grows stronger, and just like in the story, I see the branch bend in the wind and whip forward, releasing a beech seed to land beside an old log. The sun sets and rises again, sets and rises again, and slowly what was once a seed has grown into a sapling, hiding behind the fallen log. The days grow shorter, the leaves fall and soon it snows. This sequence of events is played before me, and slowly the beech tree is growing, stretching up towards the sun. With each season it speeds up and then it stops. It is spring, the leaves are starting to grow and I hear birds singing. A blackbird lands on one of the branches and starts to sing.

"Look at the blackbird," Peru says. "The blackbird is singing to the whole world, telling everyone, 'this is my territory, this is my tree, and this is where I will create life'. For this beech tree it is the first time it has supported life, life supports life. The tree will grow, the blackbird will nest and raise its young, and they will leave the nest. If a blackbird lives for four-hundred years this tree will be a home for ninety-four nesting pairs of blackbirds, year in and year out."

"OK, I think I get it," I say.

"No! You don't get it! You killed yourself, can you not understand this? How was this supposed to be a solution? You will return soon and these lessons will become ingrained in your energy. These are not words you remember, you won't one day write this as a story. You will know their meanings, The Beech Tree, Footsteps in the Sand. We give you these so you understand the evolution, how it matters and doesn't matter. It is what stops you becoming wrapped up and concerned about a world that doesn't exist. This existence isn't reality, and worrying at night about decisions you have never made and don't have control over is point-less," Peru says.

"And I will understand this by watching blackbirds in a tree?" I reply.

Peru smiles. "We are trying to teach you what to look for in life, how to see the world. Change your perception and look for the energy."

I look at the beech tree and the blackbird, tuning into their energy, and I see that the tree has a yellow, shimmering light, I look towards the base of the beech tree and into the earth, following the roots. The roots are drawing up energy from the earth, pulling the energy into the trunk and outwards onto the branches. As I watch, I see the energy transfer, the tree drawing up the energy and sending it outwards, through the blackbird. The blackbird draws the energy into itself: the energy flows through the blackbird, changes slightly before passing back out. As I look across the woods, the plants on the ground, the insects in the leaf mulch and upwards to the biggest trees, they all draw upon this golden energy and pass it back out. I am watching life, and life supports life. The day becomes stormy again and night starts to close in. The old beech tree starts to creak in the strong winds, the roots do not hold as they once did, and the tree starts to lift from the ground. The wind is relentless and growing stronger as the storm worsens, the beech tree, no longer able to hold on as it is blown over and crashes to the ground.

Eventually, the storm subsides, but the mighty beech is down. It is not long before animals come and check out the old tree, sniffing around as if paying their respects. The tree is still giving out its energy: it has changed slightly and the animals are responding to this. As the days roll on, insects appear and plants start to grow around the tree. At the root end of the beech tree, the hole in the ground has become overgrown, and a deer has given birth to a fawn. Both mother and child breathe in the energy and pass it back to each other, their energies become entwined, the process strengthens the fawn until it is able to stand and leave the cover of the fallen beech tree. Even after storms have felled the old beech tree, it continues to radiate energy and support new life. One-hundred years on, it has nearly returned to the earth and the last glow of energy rises up from the soil. A bright, strong energy passes through me, sending a rippling sensation across my energy as if I am being altered in some way.

A voice says to me, "The beech tree, the blackbird and the river, all living and so-called non-living things have a purpose. They do not confuse themselves by trying to be what they are not. They do not worry themselves about what they cannot achieve. A tree grows and it knows its purpose; to grow, to produce seeds so that others can grow. The tree knows it will provide shelter to others so they will grow too. The tree knows that, in time, it will fall, but when it falls the tree knows new life will continue to be supported in its shelter, life that it could not support when it was standing. The water in the river knows when it is ice and when it is rain, snow, clouds or the sea. The water does not worry about its form, because water knows it is always water. The blackbird needs both the water and the trees to live, life supports life. Acceptance will become ingrained in you, this knowledge will be part of your energy, and whatever form you next take, you will be the sum of this knowledge."

I watch the blackbirds come and go. They build new nests to replace last year's nest. They raise their young, every parent the same, backwards and forwards, relentlessly bringing food, helping the young to grow strong. Until one day the young blackbirds climb out of the nest, spread their wings and start to flap. They do not try to fly at first, they just flap their wings, feeling the breeze. And then they leap into the air, most of them landing clumsily on a branch, some unlucky ones even falling to the ground. But once they get that feeling of what they truly are, nothing can stop them, and it isn't long before they take to the skies. Within hours there is no more clumsiness, just majestic birds flying between the branches. They have become what they were designed to be.

2ND FLOOR

// The preparations are nearly made. You will return soon," the tramp says.

Startled, I look round. I am back in Limbo Park.

"Preparations? What preparations?" I ask. I thought I had just been prepared!

"To return. Your new opportunity. It is nearly time. You will hit the ground soon."

"What do we do?" I ask the tramp.

The tramp smiles, but her eyes look different. She is not smiling from the inside as I have seen before. The tramp opens a portal in Limbo Park. I can see a room, and darkness encroaches and starts to seep into Limbo Park. I have seen this darkness before, and I can hear the grunting of the demons. To my side is a sunny view of a suburban town, the building with twenty-two floors, and my body suspended just a couple of floors off the ground.

"What's going on? I thought this was for those who tried to stay and failed the reflection test," I say to the tramp.

"This is a plane of guilt and negative energy. The demons were once souls and in here is part of yours, the part that made you jump. A fragile soul unable to cope with the feeling of weight," the tramp says.

In front of me are moaning souls. The demons do not seem bothered by me: they are watching over their prey and feasting. As I walk, I can feel the darkness below my feet, but this time it is unable to penetrate my soles to poison me. I can feel my own strength and feel myself without fear. The energy form that I am has become stronger. I look into the shadows searching for a clue... Just what am I looking for? What is here that I mustn't leave behind? Below my feet I see footsteps in the sand, and ahead I see a dark shadow sitting on a bench. Mr Grey, a mountain I never climbed on earth. Just how do I move this mountain? I follow my footsteps and as I place each foot down I gain a glimpse of that previous life, lives past and guilt built up and collected. I have been in six wars and killed many people, I myself did not survive any of the wars and nor did I survive the scars. These burdens from past lives are heavy, as I pass one footstep I feel lightness. In this life I was a wealthy man who gave to many, I was a Roman and set up schools and hospitals. People loved me, I had a wife and children who were happy and loved me also. I lived that life feeling blessed; so great was my joy that as I pass this footstep it still glows. I look for the next glow, but it is faint. I am a fisherman somewhere in the Mediterranean, Greece, possibly, a local man. I am throwing nets over the side of the boat. I feel great contentedness. As I approach the bench nearing the end of my footsteps a demon raises its head and sniffs the air, looks at me and snarls, then bounds over to Mr Grey. Mr Grey is much darker in this room. He raises his hand and pets the demon. He looks at me, his eyes drained and tired, deep set in their sockets, his skin colourless and ragged. Mr Grey tries to smile, the corner of his mouth quivers. I hardly recognise myself as this Mr Grey; he is much more depleted of life than the one in my mind on the Earth plane. As I look at Mr Grey, his hand now resting on the demon's head, I can see the dark entering his flesh and poisoning his body. And then I see it: a thin silver line, a connection to all of the lives, including mine. Twenty-two steps, twenty-two lives we are all connected, past and present, and I have an opportunity to take the next step. My twenty-third reincarnation, but this time with no darkness, no guilt and no demon feeding off me from afar, constantly hoping I fail. I see for the first time the darkness dripping off me like tar. I am unclean, and the demon is excited by this. Mr Grey is a null and void spectator unable to help. The demon steps towards me, its claws growing. I am still. I do not know what I am supposed to do. The demon swipes at me and cuts a huge gash across my body.

The black tar starts to seep into me. I look around for the tramp or my guides, but I am on my own. I look to Mr Grey, but he is hunched over.

"Please, help me," I plead.

"Angels," Mr Grey murmurs, not looking up.

Angels, what angels? Then I remember sitting next to the angels in church when Elaine was praying for redemption. It was hypnotic, and I don't remember what happened, but I did touch the angel and make a connection, I'm sure of it. Sitting next to Mr Grey is the angel, illuminated as before.

"Beech trees know they are beech trees and do not try to be anything else. You are a soul, remember this and do not try to be anything else," the angel says to me.

The demon swipes again and again, but to no avail now. Its claws go through me.

A soul? A soul, I ask myself, what is a soul? A soul is energy, light, and a creation of the highest consciousness. A single thought of conscious energy manifested into being. It is divine light and the dark and light cannot share the same space. I feel myself again, only greater, and I start to expand my being with light. The gash on my body heals, and as the light flows out of me, it floods into the demon and it disappears. The colour is returning to Mr Grey's cheeks, and there is grass growing beneath his feet. We have returned to the park where he once left me. The rain stops, the clouds clear and the sky becomes bluer, the sun more golden than when seen from Earth. Mr Grey sits up, his eyes are bright, his trilby and coat are still grey and dusty, but he is now a colourful expression of who I am, as I once intended him to be.

"Thank you," my grey self says. "It is time for us to return."

1ST FLOOR

The new Mr Grey walks over to the building and looks at my body, suspended in the air.

"This shouldn't have happened, you were never meant to jump," Mr Grey says to me.

"It did happen though. I even tried to change it, but you won," I reply.

"I didn't win anything. You changed, you decided to let go, it was your choice. You found me and showed me this wonderful colourful explosion of life and you tried to make me vibrant and energised. I touched you and you changed. In your mind, you let go. At any time, you could have lived, chosen to live a vibrant life. Any day of the week you could have just woken up and decided, 'today I smile for the rest of my life'," Mr Grey tells me.

"You poisoned me," I say, slightly angrily.

"I did no such thing. You visited me and I showed you who and what I was. I am a manifestation you created and visited. In my world, it was always going to end up grey at the touch of a hand, but in your world it was always up to you. I am the product of twenty-two lives, the negative slowly building. In any one life you could have let me go, but you always added to the collection. Every journey you have taken, you have always collected a little more weight, never able or willing to cast it off. Believing there is some lesson to be learnt, you've kept hold of every pain, every day you never smiled, every day that didn't go your way. You held on to all those lessons. Never, not once in twenty-two lives, did you bring back the joy, the people who loved you, the friends you laughed with. I am a product of your choices and I can only be what I am. To you, I am free, rescued from the zoo, no longer being devoured by demons. If you don't let go, I will be back there as soon as you hit the floor and finish off this journey," Mr Grey tells me.

It is hard to understand what is happening. I thought I had rescued myself and had taken the next steps. Now it seems it is in vain, and as soon as I hit the floor and take the next journey Mr Grey will return to poison me again. Confused, I seek out the tramp. She is sitting in her familiar spot, looking into the wilderness.

"Every time I want you, I always find you here. Don't you have things to do?" I say.

The tramp smiles and chuckles, it's the happiest I have seen her since we met.

"Sometimes you souls are so dumb. Do you think you are talking to the whole of me?" she replies.

"The whole of you? You're in front of me I can see you!" I reply.

"I am sitting here: that is true. I am also sitting in 1083 other places right now. I am unlimited, so I will always be here for anyone who wants to talk to a tramp sitting on a log," she tells me.

"Are we the same?" I ask her.

"We are not each other, but we are the same source as are all things. We are separated by the direction we took," she tells me.

"But you're not my perception, a manifestation of me, a higher self, helping me?" I say.

The tramp stands up. "Look around. Everything you see is a perception, a manifestation, all of this exists and doesn't exist. You can see it so it exists and you can see me so I exist. What separates me and you is that I have no connection to the Earth and you think you are still there," the tramp says.

"I am still connected to the body, I have seen the cord that connects me to my body."

"Yes, connects you. It isn't you, though. You are still taking human form, you see me as a tramp, and your perception is still human. I know I am a soul, what are you?" the tramp asks.

"I'm not sure..." I reply. Which is the truth. The tramp has disappeared and I am not in Limbo Park. I am standing with Mr Grey by the building with twenty-two floors. Mr Grey is smiling and then I feel it.

Mr Grey isn't just all of my previous lives, the bad bits I have collected. He is my ego, the bit that won't let go, that doesn't want to die. He is smiling because he knows there is another ego to collect. He is what he is as I am what I am. The ego, from the beginning, learns of our past lives, collects the memories and twists the lessons, then weakens us with inner thoughts belittling ourselves, making us doubt who and what we are. The power, the strength, belong to them. And this is the illusion: as long as my perception is from the ego, I am an illusion. I am a soul, I am connected here because I believed I am, because I believe I am bound to Earth, bound to the body I walk around in. I am not bound to this earth or this body. I am free and I have to realise that. My body has fallen twenty-one floors and this is the last stop. All that is left is the pavement.

Thud. Followed by screams. Thud doesn't really do it justice, in a split second all of my bones broke, my internal organs were stopped so suddenly they became puree. My ribs collapsed and pierced my skin, allowing the puree to seep out. The side of my head that hit the ground has been pushed inside my skull, the pressure has forced some of my brain through my ear canal, and one of my eyes has popped out. The people who were filming Angie and Gary fighting have stopped. Some are screaming, some are stunned with silence, a few start to look upwards to see where I have fallen from. Angie hasn't noticed at all and has run down the road. Gary, who was surprised by Angie's retaliation, has now started to vomit from the sight of my body on the ground. Many of the people who were so filled with joy watching Angie and Gary fight, watching another person hurt, are now crying, shocked to their souls and unsure of what to do next.

I too am unsure. My body is dead and I am alive. Preparations were put in place yet here I am alive, alive! And a ripple begins, slowly the thought settles, I am alive, I am real, I rescued Mr Grey and now he can stay with the body. No more illusions, and as the thought resonates I feel my expansion to the whole. I am complete: there are no barriers. My higher self is also in many places, like the tramp, unlimited, no restrictions. I sense all of the souls I am, how we are and have been connected, just how many lives I am living right now. The limitless soul does not have the boundary of time and nor do I. Before I start the next phase of my journey, I am reconnected with my higher self, a form that is pure and has knowledge beyond all conceptions of possibility. My brief connection is expansive, there are many fragments to my soul, and I have a spiritual family, unconnected to the one on Earth. I am ready again to start the next separation, only this time my energy will remember the cycle of life and not be phased by the world I am going to enter. I can see Angie and the life form she carries, and I make my journey back. I fill this little body and attach myself. I will soon lose the understanding that everything is connected. Everything is just an expression of thought, manifested by our own abilities. To be able to receive the ultimate experience of life, it is more than just knowing that we are souls in a body being transported. It is realising we are life itself and understanding there is a purpose. The purpose is to live: how you find your joy is the journey, how you feel about this is the choice. The energy of joy will always attract more joy and this attraction is all powerful. To be able to smile from inside will connect you to the higher you and it will not be a miracle, just a simple choice. It won't be found by jumping off a building, it will be found by living.

EPILOGUE

HOW TO TRAIN YOUR PET LIZARD

MEET YOUR LIZARD

Unless you have specialist training, or you were born super chilled out. You're an impulsive emotional being.

Even if you don't believe it, we're all guilty of having a brain, despite what you may have heard, or think you've witnessed. A common phrase used to describe the Limbic part of the brain, is the "Lizard Brain". Having a Lizard in your brain is not the important part but understanding how it controls your reactions to your environment, is vital. This limbic part of the brain enabled us to evolve from tree dwellers, to the people we are today. The lizard kept you fearful, and fear kept you alive.

Eating, drinking, sex, fear, flight and fight all come from this part of our brain, and it's primitive, hence why we refer to it as our lizard or reptilian brain. It also holds you back, and it's supposed to. The key to human survival is having a part of our brain which tells us to be cautious, to fear the unknown.

The unknown at the beginning of our evolution was, what is waiting to eat me and where is it hiding. As we became more tribal, this also took the role of peer pressure. If you stand out from the crowd you endanger the community. If you endanger your community, they will throw you out, and without this protection, you will be eaten.

We must thank our Lizard Brain for doing a great job, allowing humans to evolve and move through time to where you are today. It is also time to gain some perspective and learn how to train it. You want your pet lizard to be house trained.

If you are doing something new, there is a chance the lizard thinks you are going to die and takes appropriate action.

When you hesitate, procrastinate, worry, become anxious, fear what others think of you, believe likes on social media are important, self loathe, be critical of yourself, the list can go on and on. This is the lizard trying to stop you from getting killed. It doesn't understand your life is not in danger. It's not its job to understand, its job is to keep you alive. If you feel pleasure the lizard is in a happy state, feel judged, and the lizard becomes defensive.

When someone is mean to you and you take it to heart. This is the lizard thinking you are going to be thrown out of the tribe, and then be eaten.

When you want to learn something new and you get self-doubt, fear of failure, put things off, worry or become isolated. This is the lizard thinking you are going to be eaten.

These feelings are the lizard protecting you. It doesn't understand you are not in danger. It doesn't know you are fine, but you must take steps to teach the lizard how to behave. Just like you would a puppy. You take it home and start with basic toilet training, and some basic commands. You must do the same with the lizard. You must house train it!

To best train the lizard, we need to understand the importance of language and how we use it. Learn to see between the words and their meaning, and how we speak to ourselves.

Take the words "Reason, and Excuse"

A reason means *a cause, explanation, or justification for an action or event.*

An Excuse means *a reason or explanation given to justify a fault or offence.*

Read the two sentences and see how similar they are. The main difference is the meaning we put behind these words, and the context in which we use them. Over the years I have often observed this behaviour in people. A person will have a reason why they can't do something or make a change. It's not an excuse, it's never an excuse, because that would be negative, and can't be their fault.

An event has happened, or a fear has cast doubt and the lizard has kicked in and now you think you are going to be eaten.

You are not going to be eaten!

Here's another way to observe the lizard, and how it helps you survive. You are hunting, there is potential danger and the lizard (you) is alert. Your senses are honed, and you are in the zone. You see your prey (dinner) and you react. Later that night you are "Eating" You have survived, because you used the basic instincts of the lizard to aid you. To be at your best.

And unless you're playing a game of hide and seek with an actual lion in your local supermarket, you don't need these skills when you are walking down the food aisle shopping. But it doesn't mean your pet lizard isn't making you nervous while you're trying to work out if you need that 3 for 1 offer on tinned pineapple.

COUNT YOUR BLESSINGS

Today you hear all about positive thinking, gratitude, what are you grateful for? Affirmations. And it's normally attached to a, hashtag health guru who lives in the sun and is on a mission to save you and the planet.

My grandparents, and their grandparents also believed the same thing. They called it "Count your blessings". It was simpler, and in those days, more easily understood.

To give this context, in 18th Century Sweden 1 in 3 children under the age of 5 died.

In early 19th Century Germany every 2nd child died.

Having a child was not a blessing, it was a necessity, otherwise humans would have died out. Here's a harrowing perspective. If you have more than three children and one of them hadn't died. You were rare!

And this world we live in is unrecognisable to the one my grandparents grew up in. If you didn't have a job, you starved to death, if you got sick and couldn't work you starved to death. The list of nightmares goes on. This is why the phrase "Count your blessings" had real meaning. Because they could relate to it and understand it. Everyone (without exception) was affected by a different reality to the one you and I have, and without their experience how can we relate to the meaning.

Can you imagine the having a roof over your head, enough food on the table for everyone to have a meal? Yeah, of course you can.

Can you imagine having a roof over your head as a luxury, a meal on the table a blessing, you don't know where tomorrows meals are coming from and only one of your children is sick, and only one has died? And you think you are blessed! You wake up in the morning and believe you have a life to be grateful for.

It is not my intention to be cynical of the hashtag guru. I'm all for positive thinking, affirmations, and gratitude. Part of training your pet lizard is getting out of a negative mindset and creating a positive inner voice.

Have you ever been in a car accident, and afterwards realised it could have been much worse? For a short period of time, you feel grateful to be alive. Or you're in a near miss, and nothing happens, but you know 1 minute earlier you were stood where an object fell, or a car struck. Again, you get a sense of wellbeing, a sense I am lucky to be here. Without realising it you have counted your blessings.

I believe one of the reasons society struggles to mentally thrive in the world today, is because we have never had it so good. Queuing in a coffee shop is a source of frustration. We get angry because we must wait, and the indecisive person in front of us is so spoilt for choice, they can't make up their mind, and you're not allowed to kill them!

Practice happiness, understand the little things, learn to count your blessings. Try different things, and figure out what helps you feel, lucky, blessed, happy to be in your world.

The best practice I have which works for me, and it's not the answer to all things. But sometimes I remind myself of my worse days, the times I never want to relive. The dark days, when I would have swapped anything to be somewhere else, to be someone else. Then I remind myself, the life of the guy whose fingers are tapping these keys and writing this paragraph, once dreamed of being who I am today. I wished my life could have been this good.

I will think of times spent laughing with friends, my pet's past and present.

What I would have once done to count the blessings I have today.

This isn't applicable to everyone. People by comparison have different lives, and varying degrees of difficulty throughout their life. Sometimes it seems some people never get troubled, and others seem to live under a storm cloud. That's life and how it works. The dice roll differently for everyone, and not everyone rolls sixes.

Is that supposed to make you feel better? No!

It's the truth, and the more we work with our truth, the more integrity we have in our life, and the less we resent the world around us. Life cannot be sunshine and roses every day, for everyone, it's not possible, but life is a damn sight easier than it's ever been.

There are more resources, more tools, more education, more opportunities, more access to interests, than there has ever been, and you are in complete control of how you want to utilise this.

Stop messing around, stop bitching, the clock ticks and you are going to die. Count your blessings, learn what makes you happy, and have a great life.

THE ECHO CHAMBER

Your echo chamber is a source of comfort, and like the lizard it has a purpose, but it can also get in your way. There are two types of echo chamber.

The first. Doing the same thing again and again but expecting a different outcome. And if you've heard someone say "But I thought" it's a sign that no thinking has taken place which take's responsibility for their actions or the outcomes. If they had given the problem genuine thought, the outcome they wanted would have happened. If it hadn't they would accept responsibility and say I messed up and explain how they messed up.

Second. The most common echo chamber is always listening to the same opinions. You only listen to what you want to hear. You never risk being proved wrong, you never listen to an opinion outside of your beliefs, and you never leave room for a change of mind.

The best example of this I know is religion and Science. Ask any Christian and they will tell you God and Jesus exists.

Ask a scientist and they will tell you about the big bang and no evidence.

I am neither a practising Christian, nor am I a scientist, but I know this. The bible can be traced back to its origins, it has a time line. The Christian Bible has two sections, the Old Testament and the New Testament. The Old Testament is the original Hebrew Bible, the sacred scriptures of the Jewish faith, written at different times between 1200 and 165 BC. The New Testament books were written by Christians in the first century AD. There is also Moses Pentateuch, and other writings.

I also know, mainly from listening to Neill DeGrasse Tyson. The universe is continually expanding, and they don't know why. They do not know what was before the big bang, or what caused it.

The point being neither side has true evidence that one exists or how the other happened, however both sides are prepared to argue to the point of hatred, they are right and the other is wrong.

Of course, using religion against science is provocative, and deliberately so. You must take note of what you are listening too and don't be fooled by so called experts. Especially if these experts are on TV telling you about the future.

CONFIDENCE

I f you can learn to be better at one thing, you have started on the path to one of the most important steps in life. Building the foundations to become better at anything. Learn how to do one new thing, and then learn how to do it better. This is the most important step, the foundation to everything you need in life. If you can grasp the idea, and understand the basic concept of learning something new, you have the basic plan for successful living. (Later I discuss how to define success)

Understand the ticking clock, and it never stops ticking. It distorts your perception and allows the lizard to cast doubt, eat your inspiration and puts you back in the cave safe and sound before you can get eaten. Nothing is going to eat you.

Everything takes time, you can only take incremental steps to achieve something new and become better at it. There are no big leaps, at the beginning, if at all. Successful people understand this, and they understand time is their friend. They work with it. They create a timeline of where they want to be and decide on the incremental steps they will need to take to get there. It really is this simple. A successful person knows, anything they want to achieve will take time. They never think it will take too long. Results takes the time they take, and time is on my side.

The wrong perception can kill an idea before it even starts, by thinking it will take too long.

Confidence can seem unattainable. It can be misread, the loudest person in the room isn't always the most confident. When a person shouts, or belittles others, it is common for this to be their learnt coping mechanism to feel safe. Have you ever had that friend who's great company on their own, but changes in the crowd?

How do you attain confidence?

Repetition, repetition, repetition, and in case you're wondering repetition!

And time! Repetition and time equals confidence.

Listen to any interview with the most successful sports people and they will talk about the hours spent practising. Hours spent doing something again, and again. Without exception, they will describe how they took their talent and made it exceptional. They literally taught themselves how not to fail. They did something so frequently, they no longer knew how to do it wrong.

They will have failed more times trying successfully do one thing than you will have tied your shoe laces in your lifetime. And every time they failed, they tried again.

Here's another thing you must do. It's probably the biggest reason people fail. Almost every time. They fail to make a start.

So, just make a start. Get out of bed and just get on with it. Below is a list of silly things for you to read. Try and read it in a silly voice. It's just a fun thing to think about and offer a perspective on time. I would love to hear from you the readers, what else you would add to this list.

You cannot grow old without living for a long time.

Every black belt started as a white belt.

Every driver has passed a road test (hopefully)

Every marathon runner had to start by buying running shoes.

Every teacher had a first day at school.

Every adult had to learn to tie their shoes.

Every doctor was given medicine by their parents.

Every politician had to become old enough to vote.

Every language starts with the first word.

A plane can't fly if it doesn't take off.

A seed was planted so you could eat an apple. (Technically not true, as apples are grown from cuttings)

As I said, its just a little silly fun, but the meaning? Is to help you understand perception, time, practice, failing. You need all of this to gain confidence. Read the next paragraph carefully and allow it to digest.

A stand-up comic is a person who goes on stage to make people laugh at them. The more successful you are the more people are laughing. It's easy to think the comic is controlling the laughter, and everyone is laughing with them. That's only true when they have failed enough times to become good at their craft. Every comedian bombed, and had an audience laughing at them, not with them. How much courage does it take to get up on stage and be the joke, before people laugh at your jokes.

One of the key ingredients to confidence and a better life. Is to get out of your own way and get over yourself. It does not matter if you fail, it does not matter if you don't get it right 1st time, 2nd time 3rd time and so on. It just does not matter and remind your lizard it doesn't matter.

SMILE

Smile! It's as simple as that. Train yourself to smile. Happiness is a mindset, and how to be happy is up to you.

The brain recalls memories and experiences, and when your inner chatter doesn't suit the mood you want, change it. Ask yourself some questions.

When was the last time I laughed?

What made me laugh 10 years ago?

When did I last feel inspired?

Who was the last person I admired?

What's my favourite animal?

Puppies or kittens?

Practice questions to recall happiness. The brain functions on routine, and rehearsed drills. This is the most efficient way to bring immediate answers. Become better organised and create a filing system in your mind designed by you, to access the information. To be in control of the conversations you want to hear.

Describe your favourite emotion, and what you are doing when you feel this.

Take a note of what your body is doing, and how your body feels to you when you are felling happy. Focus some attention on this, learn to listen to your body. What makes your body relax, feel alive? It will make you feel happy.

UNDERSTAND HAPPINESS

I f you can understand your happiness, well...

I will make a bold statement, a promise. If you can understand your own personal happiness and be willing to work on it. I promise you the most fulfilled life you could imagine.

To start with think about what makes you happy, if you're serious you will make a list. If you only thought about it and didn't write the list. I know you are not serious. People who want change, will write the list.

I am going to make an assumption, everything on the list is external.

A sunset, more money, holiday, clothes, TV show, great partner, better job, weekends off, the list could go on and on.

Can you write a list of things which make you happy and cost nothing?

If I asked you how you know when you are happy. What would you write?

How do you know when you feel happy?

What are you doing?

How do you feel?

What's happening in your body?

Internally what is going on?

It's important to understand this because when we externalise happiness we can lose sight of how happiness feels. Simply I might admire the sun setting when I am on holiday, but not appreciate the same sun setting when I look out of the window at home.

I have stretched the experience. The sunset I saw on holiday was great because I was on holiday. Then I saw it again with a drink, the next time from a beach side restaurant, the time after that I had spent the day diving and was sooooo relaxed!

Alternatively, I might be getting stressed out trying to upgrade my house or my car, believing it will make me happier. When in fact my house is fine, the car is fine. But a 2nd holiday with that sunset would feel amazing.

Or the house is fine, the car is fine, holidays are ok, but I would love more time off. Would I be happier working less and having more time to myself?

What you value can become priceless! But when you chase a need, without understanding what you are trying to fix. It will always be broken.

When you teach yourself to listen to the signs your body is giving you, to recognise those signals, they become like gut instincts. What's more, when your body recoils at an idea, you listen! Teaching yourself to listen to your body, is the most effective way to take care of your physical self.

HAPPINESS IS A FLOWER

Sad people died long before their body failed. There happiness was poisoned, never allowed to blossom, to bloom into something wonderous. An infectious energy which spread life into their every cell and made their DNA tingle with delight.

Happiness is like a flower. Tend to it, give it space to grow and feed it, then it will flourish, and thrive. It will grow strong, and weather any storm.

Ignore it, let the weeds take over and it will die. And no matter how many times you try to replant it, the soil is poisoned, and soil needed for the roots to make their foundations is toxic, and the flower will never be able to grow.

This is what really kills people. Their life dictated by outside forces. Weeds which crushed them, bullied themselves until they lost their personal space. The identity of who they were. It doesn't take much. The clock ticks, and the years pass.

You think you have your whole life ahead of you, and then one day you wake up and it's not there. The ability to smile, to be happy from within. It can seem like life has trampled on your dreams and ambitions. It didn't, you didn't tend your personal space in life's garden. You didn't look after You.

If you feel this and know what this means. It's not too late for you. In truth it's never too late really, but you must start tending to your own personal garden if you want to be able to grow and bloom brightly, and for no one else, other than yourself. Sure, you can be a good example to the kids, siblings or your partner. But do it for you, set your own standards, and do it before the poison can't be cured.

GLASSES

B e careful, mindful and aware of what you see. When your eyesight starts to fail, becomes less than 20 20 vision. You make an appointment to see an optician. Once it is confirmed the optician will sit down and discuss options with you.

Life's lens is not so transparent, and harder to fix if you didn't notice you had gone blind.

Beware the lens of the media, from politics to the news about other countries. History is littered with deliberate untruths which suited agenda of a media mogul.

Leicester City won the premier league title in 2015–2016. Against all the odds. The experts said it couldn't happen.

In 2011 Brad Pitt starred in the film *Money Pitt*. A film based on the Oakland Athletics baseball team and their 2002 season. A baseball team with one of the lowest wage structures nearly won the season. They recruited players under a system called the "Sabermetrics" a statistic-based programme. Previously people picked who they thought was the best, so if you looked ugly, especially when batting. You were unlikely to be picked for a big team.

This was 2002, the statistics had been around since the beginning of baseball. Now all of baseball is run on this system.

1920's great depression, 1986 Black Wednesday followed by a session, 2007 Bank collapse, followed by housing collapse. Every one of these financial implosions went against the advice of the experts.

The reason this is so important? What is an expert?

Experts! *Expert, noun. Meaning: A person who is very knowledgeable about or skilful in a particular area.*

In other words, the people who were experts in their field did not see it coming and did not predict it. They all said they did not understand what or why it was happening. In truth, they were looking at the wrong parameters and making judgments on these rules, or they were trying to predict the future, by looking into the past.

If you see something and it doesn't make sense. It does make sense you are just looking through the wrong glasses. Go and get an eye test! What are you not seeing?

Worse still it was being reported as fact and truth, and this is how we become blind.

SALMON

WHY SALMON?

If you were a salmon, you have one definition of success. You were born in a river, swam downstream. Lived in the sea, grew strong, survived predators long enough to one day return to the river you swam out of and then start swimming upwards. You will swim upstream, to the spawning grounds and then mate. This journey is so hard, it will kill you. If you succeed against all the odds, you are guaranteed to die.

Success!

Define what you think is successful. Successful to **YOU**! And you alone. You are not a salmon and your only responsibility is to define your own success.

Describe what success means to you?

Describe why success means this to you?

Describe what success looks and feels like?

Describe how you will know you are successful?

Describe how this success will make you feel fulfilled?

Success can be our Achilles heel and most often this trips people up, especially when we compare our success to other people. Or judge our success by an emotional response caused by someone's cruel words.

If you are not mindful of the rules you put in place. You will die trying to be more successful than someone you didn't want to be. Regardless of what rules you put in place, if they are based on something outside of yourself. Someone else will always be more successful than you.

Fulfilment, on the other hand. Is completely about you, controlled by you and can only be compared to you.

If you make the goal of your success to be fulfilled, how does this change? And how does it look different?

INSPIRATION

When someone has made the news for doing an incredible human challenge. They are asked what inspired them or who has inspired you? This is asked to give us the audience, some insight into what triggered the spark that made this ordinary person so driven they rose to the top of their game, to be better than those around them, to become the person they wanted to be.

Have you been inspired?

It is important to understand inspiration is just a thought, a feeling. Inspiration is the muse sat on your shoulder whispering a suggestion, something you might try and hopefully put a smile on your face, give you a sense of achievement or an opportunity to explore in your imagination the person you might want to become. It is the spark to hopefully ignite a passion from within and it comes in many ways.

Sometimes we are watching a TV chef produce a mouth-watering dish and as we watch they take us step by step, through the process. There are little hints to make it better, alternative ingredients you can try to make subtle changes to the taste. This process convinces us we CAN do that too. You and I can cook.

I felt inspired to raise money with a friend we cycled from London to Paris. The process changed my life for six months with the planning, the training, and the fundraising. I met some incredible people, achieved a great sense of purpose overcoming the challenges, and became absorbed in something new. I felt proud of myself, discovered a new me and one of the many extra bonuses. The process remapped my mind.

I had taken something I didn't know how to do and made it possible.

Inspiration can be for any reason; maybe you just want to pull yourself out of a rut. What is important, is to understand your inspiration and let your imagination play with it. This will take you to your motivation. You have a reason to look for inspiration, you have yourself and you need to pick yourself up and dust yourself off. It doesn't have to be a big challenge, it could be a course or a new a hobby. Maybe you don't know, so look through your local paper at what's on in your local college and pick five small taster classes. You will be surprised what you may enjoy.

When you set goals, you become a different person on the journey to achieving them

MOTIVATION

You have been inspired and now you need to motivate yourself. So why do you want this, and this applies to anything in your life. We go to work because we are either motivated by our jobs or motivated to pay our bills.

Motivation is why you make the list of the ingredients from the TV chef and then cook the meal. You have motivated yourself to do something you were inspired by. If you played with your inspired idea, hopefully you will have invoked new ideas, images and feelings to help motivate you. You want this! You want this outcome and you want this end result. These are your motivation factors. If inspiration is the foundation, then motivation is the building blocks.

When motivation takes us, it can feel like a surge of energy and we gain a new zest for life. Often inspiration and motivation can give us a determination to get things done, to change our routine. So why do you want this?

Be clear about your motivation and use this as your target. Aim for your target and keep going until you hit your target. Take time to understand your motivation. Are you trying for a healthier lifestyle? Do you have an upcoming social event? Never lose sight of your target and use this to motivate yourself. You can adapt, change your focus. Hopefully as time goes on you will make changes, reach further and be inspired to try something else. By the time you reach your target you will have discovered how you have made the changes, friends and family will have noticed the difference. You will have become the person you inspired to be.

You have to redesign your life, invest in your lifestyle.

Map out your week, your month and your year. How does it compare to your old life? And how can it look now, where can you be one year from now.

You may not be feeling too confident right now. This can take time and courage; your inspiration and motivation will carry you over the line if you allow it to. The fear can overwhelm you if your pay too much attention to it. Once you have achieved just the smallest thing you are already on the way. Investigating what you may want to do, finding that inspiration starts to build your confidence. You don't have to challenge yourself to climb a mountain.

Go to the cinema have some ME time. Art class, gardening, read a book, do anything to throw off the shackles and then commit to it.

> *Focused people don't need motivation.*
> *Motivated people need focus.*

DISCIPLINE

When you take inspiration and motivation and you put them together, you're a fired-up person ready to take on the world, to achieve something for yourself to finally overcome an obstruction. You will feel like you can smash down walls, sign up for a marathon and make the changes in yourself you always knew you were capable of.

Discipline is how you get there. Discipline, discipline and more discipline. It doesn't matter what you are trying to change, it doesn't matter what you are trying to achieve, to get there and to reach your target you will need discipline. And here's the thing. If you get up in the morning, get washed, go to work every day, raise kids, watch TV, eat food, read magazines, spend hours on the internet you already have discipline. You know it as your routine. Your habits!

Discipline is about changing your routine. Discipline is about taking your inspiration and motivation and deciding today I am doing this instead, tomorrow I am doing this instead and the next day I will be doing something else that isn't part of my old routine. You have become so disciplined into holding onto what you once had it could be holding you in a never-ending cycle. Only you can be responsible for you.

When you make sure you don't miss a TV programme, that's discipline. Those little treats which built up and became your daily routine this is discipline. I know you will read this and say I am talking about habits and you are correct. A habit requires discipline and it is important for you to understand this. To break your habit, you have to change your discipline and become disciplined in the new practise you are trying to achieve.

Discipline and habit cross over. Ask any driven person and they will tell you it started with an idea and then they set about doing it. They turned their discipline into habit.

Think of the deadlines you meet at work. The reason you always make the deadline is because you disciplined yourself into the habit. Paying bills, managing your finances, every essential activity you stay on top of is because you turned your discipline into a habit.

Discipline will maintain your focus, discipline will get you through your first day and discipline will take you through the first week, months and years. Discipline will make it happen, it will make you.

ILLUSIONS

Let's discuss illusions, and how we are all aware of them. The classics are. I eat healthy, exercise and I am overweight. Unless it is a medical condition. It's a lie.

I don't have enough money and I can't make ends meet. In reality they have big TV, Sky, mobile phones, the latest gadgets, more clothes than space, they buy lunch every day, they eat takeaways etc.

It's not my fault. This applies to so many things. People blame situations for their lives and while they are blaming the world, they are convincing themselves of the illusion. If you live in the West, almost every aspect of your life can be controlled by you.

Time! People say they do not have time. If you watch TV, play computer games etc. you have free time.

Time! It takes too long. This nearly always applies to education, training or saving money. Nothing takes too long, it takes what it takes and that is it. The issue is simple. You are going to die; how do you want to get there? On your own terms or bitching about the life you had with your last breath. It will happen quicker than you think.

It's a little known, rarely discussed fact. When people want something, and set that target, or goal. Time does not come into it. They breakdown what needs to be done, create a strategy to make it happen and take little steps to get there.

So, here's the plan.

MAKE A PLAN!

When do you want to start?

How are you going to track your progress?

What are the incremental steps?

How long can it take?

How many years?

The clock is ticking, and it does not stop. If you think feeling silly hurts, or people laughing at you hurts. Wait until you run out of time and you haven't done any of things you wanted to do. You already feel this pain inside, magnify it by how many decades you have left. That's real pain, that's real failure, and it can't be cured or undone.

Another point of view, and this is for perspective only. How many years do you think you have left?

How many years do you have to have before you stop pleasing other people's opinions of who you should be.

Now is the time to do something for YOU. To give yourself a target, to do something new, learn something new or visit somewhere you have dreamed of.

What do you want?
Who do you want to be?
What is your new dream?

In the next section are the exercises for you to carry out. And this is where a you can trip up and let yourself down. You make an excuse and just don't do them, and then sit there a week later wondering why you're not feeling better about yourself. Why nothing has changed. The reason for this is because you're not willing to change. You know who you are, prove me wrong!

The clock does not hold back time
because of your excuses.

The clock never, ever stops ticking.

The clock is not waiting for you.

You are going to die!

EXERCISES

1. UNDERSTAND WHO YOU ARE!

It is important to understand your worth as a person. This creates the foundation of self-worth and recognising the skills, talent, gifts you offer and how you offer them. Just as important is recognising, in reality you're not a genocidal maniac, a war lord or some prophet of doom.

If you were looking in a magic mirror and you were able to see your best self; how would you want to see yourself?

It's ok to feel vulnerable this enables you to be honest with yourself. True to who you are. You can then address and tweak things, so seeing yourself in a better light can be more comfortable, and you become less vulnerable in yourself. Sometimes it's just an unpractised skill. Practising how me might appear to ourselves in a magic mirror, getting a picture of who we want to be, is key to getting there.

If you're unsure, describe what you would like to see.

Honesty is key. If you are lying to yourself, why? Can you imagine a better version of yourself as a reflection in the mirror? If you can't. Describe where these feelings come from.

This is a gateway to understanding your fears, and every person you know has these fears.

Judge your own fears, dig into them, and find out if they are real. (By judge I mean be aware)

Is this the lizard dragging up an old feeling, or testing boundaries to see if it can take over again?

TO WRITE OR TO SPEAK

I n this first exercise I want you to either write or speak, and if you speak, record yourself for a minimum of 5 minutes. And then listen back to yourself.

I want you to write 300 plus positive words about yourself. Appreciating yourself has a direct carry over into your life and the people around you. They benefit from this directly, and you will begin to appreciate how valuable you are. The barriers you may come up against are probably the same barriers everyone comes up against. Or your lizard thinks you're going to get eaten.

2. DESCRIBE HOW DO YOU WANT TO BE IDENTIFIED?

I f someone was doing a review of you, describe what you would like to hear? And why? Does any of it connect with your vulnerabilities? Does your daily life reflect who you are, or your fears?

Knowing who you want to be enables you to create the structures and the patterns to create this person and highlights when you are reacting to your vulnerabilities. Knowing this, will be one of the most freeing experiences you will ever have.

Knowing what you would like to hear and why. Helps you to create a foundation to build a strong platform. What motivates you to work, to study? It can also identify areas which are not being fulfilled or being misunderstood.

This insight creates something you can change. A personal plan or a business, it's the same principles. If you have a clear idea of how people want to talk about you. You can create a strategy to enable this to happen.

Be mindful of false expectations. No one can be liked by everyone, no matter how great you are, you can't make someone love you. You can't be 6ft 4 if your 5ft.

3. DESCRIBE HOW YOU DEMONSTRATE WHAT YOUR VALUES ARE

Let's identity what you are doing and cross reference with the work in the first question? It will either support what you do well and help you feel better about yourself or it will highlight how your holding back and what you need to learn and change.

Again, we're raising our awareness.

The obvious one again is people who want to be liked by everyone, and don't understand it's not possible, and where is the integrity in this. Companies make this mistake. A Brand can often undo themselves by trying to spread across several markets and lose focus and dilute their product. Their brand loyalty comes from Not trying to be popular but delivering what their existing customers expect.

Swap brands for friends, and! We all know people who lie, or drain our energy, they try to please everyone, or they're not reliable. We always try to avoid them. If you don't, you should.

4. DESCRIBE WHY YOUR VALUES ARE IMPORTANT TO YOU

This should be the easiest part. It will either reinforce why you love what you do or inspire you to try something new.

Let's revisit the mirror and look at the person you wish to see in your reflection. How would this version of you explain why these values are important?

LET'S RECAP

1. Understand who you are!
2. Describe how do you want to be identified
3. Describe how you demonstrate what your values are
4. Describe why is this is important to you

TWO LETTERS

There are two letters! These letters are intended to bring you to your final conclusions. As I said earlier, if you are serious about change, if you really want it. You will do this, and I would recommend you do it every year.

LETTER 1

I want you to imagine you are 70 years old. If you are 20, you really must be honest with yourself and imagine who you have turned into. Is this the person you want to become? (If you are older, like me. Imagine your future, however far you wish to project forward)

Describe how do you feel, what do you look like, where do you live, what are you angry about, what are you happy about?

Describe how your body feels, how are your relationships, what aches, what are you stressing about?

Money, finances, family, the roof over your head, where your next meal is coming from?

What are you regretting, the hours you worked or the sunsets you missed, the hours in the office, or hours which were for you, what did you do enough of, what do you wish you spent more time on?

Has the clock ticked, and the decades passed? Have enough years been lost you will finally use some for yourself.

Embrace this, really describe who you are, give it some thought. Imagine who you are, where you are. Who do you remind yourself of, are you who you wanted to be?

Could you have been kinder to yourself?

LETTER 2

When you are ready, write another to letter yourself, a letter from your older self. Offer advice, be honest, tell yourself what your younger present self must do, what to ignore, what doesn't matter and what is important.

After a week. Imagine again you are this person and reread the letter. This time write a letter thanking yourself because you did what?

What was the advice and how did you follow it?

Describe what you started doing.

Describe what you stopped doing?

And in case you didn't notice. It's three letters. Surprise!

AUTHOR'S REQUEST

Many of us have had dark times, and it is possible you have read this book, and you are having a terrible time in your life, a terrible time right now. You may be in search of answers, answers that will lead to help. I understand.

You are not crazy.

If you are feeling like enough is enough and you don't think you can carry on, I implore you to try and reach out for help. I know, friends and family always promise they will listen, and they rarely understand just what we are going through.

This can make us feel alone. You are not on your own.

I ask you to not to give up, to try, just once more to reach out. Please, just try to reach out once more. In your country there will be an organisation, a helpline, a person. A real person who wants to listen to you.

Please give life one more chance, a chance for your life to get better. I know, if you are in that dark place it doesn't seem like life can be better.

If you have reached that place. You have nothing left to loose, speak to someone and you could save a life, your life.

Give this life a chance, tomorrow has every chance to be a better day, if you just let it.

You might be the future voice which brings a person back.

Please, you have the strength, you really do. Don't be alone. Ask for help.

You can call the Samaritans on:

116 123 (UK)

116 123 (ROI)

www.samaritans.org

Whoever you are
Whereever you are from
Whatever deity you believe
Please be blessed
And take care.
Thank you for reading